Ikenaga 2 Jos Leys

"A relatively simple formula can generate immensely complex images."– **Jos Leys**

Investigations
IN NUMBER, DATA, AND SPACE®

Glenview, Illinois • Boston, Massachusetts
Chandler, Arizona • Upper Saddle River, New Jersey

The Investigations curriculum was developed by TERC, Cambridge, MA.

This material is based on work supported by the National Science Foundation ("NSF") under Grant No. ESI-0095450. Any opinions, findings, and conclusions or recommendations expressed in this material are those of the author(s) and do not necessarily reflect the views of the National Science Foundation.

ISBN-13: 978-0-328-60024-3

ISBN-10: 0-328-60024-5

1 2 3 4 5 6 7 8 9 10 V003 14 13 12 11 10

Co-Principal Investigators

Susan Jo Russell

Karen Economopoulos

Authors

Lucy Wittenberg
Director Grades 3–5

Karen Economopoulos
Director Grades K–2

Virginia Bastable
(SummerMath for Teachers,
Mt. Holyoke College)

Katie Hickey Bloomfield

Keith Cochran

Darrell Earnest

Arusha Hollister

Nancy Horowitz

Erin Leidl

Megan Murray

Young Oh

Beth W. Perry

Susan Jo Russell

Deborah Schifter
(Education
Development Center)

Kathy Sillman

Note: Unless otherwise noted, all contributors listed above were staff of the Education Research Collaborative at TERC during their work on the curriculum. Other affiliations during the time of development are listed.

Administrative Staff

Amy Taber
Project Manager

Beth Bergeron

Lorraine Brooks

Emi Fujiwara

Contributing Authors

Denise Baumann

Jennifer DiBrienza

Hollee Freeman

Paula Hooper

Jan Mokros

Stephen Monk
(University of Washington)

Mary Beth O'Connor

Judy Storeygard

Cornelia Tierney

Elizabeth Van Cleef

Carol Wright

Technology

Jim Hammerman

Classroom Field Work

Amy Appell

Rachel E. Davis

Traci Higgins

Julia Thompson

Collaborating Teachers

This group of dedicated teachers carried out extensive field testing in their classrooms, met regularly to discuss issues of teaching and learning mathematics, provided feedback to staff, welcomed staff into their classrooms to document students' work, and contributed both suggestions and written material that has been incorporated into the curriculum.

Bethany Altchek

Linda Amaral

Kimberly Beauregard

Barbara Bernard

Nancy Buell

Rose Christiansen

Chris Colbath-Hess

Lisette Colon

Kim Cook

Frances Cooper

Kathleen Drew

Rebeka Eston Salemi

Thomas Fisher

Michael Flynn

Holly Ghazey

Susan Gillis

Danielle Harrington

Elaine Herzog

Francine Hiller

Kirsten Lee Howard

Liliana Klass

Leslie Kramer

Melissa Lee Andrichak

Kelley Lee Sadowski

Jennifer Levitan

Mary Lou LoVecchio

Kristen McEnaney

Maura McGrail

Kathe Millett

Florence Molyneaux

Amy Monkiewicz

Elizabeth Monopoli

Carol Murray

Robyn Musser

Christine Norrman

Deborah O'Brien

Timothy O'Connor

Anne Marie O'Reilly

Mark Paige

Margaret Riddle

Karen Schweitzer

Elisabeth Seyferth

Susan Smith

Debra Sorvillo

Shoshanah Starr

Janice Szymaszek

Karen Tobin

JoAnn Trauschke

Ana Vaisenstein

Yvonne Watson

Michelle Woods

Mary Wright

Advisors

Deborah Lowenberg Ball,
University of Michigan

Hyman Bass, Professor of Mathematics and Mathematics Education
University of Michigan

Mary Canner, Principal, Natick Public Schools

Thomas Carpenter, Professor of Curriculum and Instruction,
University of Wisconsin-Madison

Janis Freckmann, Elementary Mathematics Coordinator,
Milwaukee Public Schools

Lynne Godfrey, Mathematics Coach,
Cambridge Public Schools

Ginger Hanlon, Instructional Specialist in Mathematics,
New York City Public Schools

DeAnn Huinker, Director, Center for Mathematics and
Science Education Research, University of Wisconsin-Milwaukee

James Kaput, Professor of Mathematics, University of
Massachusetts-Dartmouth

Kate Kline, Associate Professor, Department of Mathematics
and Statistics, Western Michigan University

Jim Lewis, Professor of Mathematics,
University of Nebraska-Lincoln

William McCallum, Professor of Mathematics,
University of Arizona

Harriet Pollatsek, Professor of Mathematics,
Mount Holyoke College

Debra Shein-Gerson, Elementary Mathematics Specialist,
Weston Public Schools

Gary Shevell, Assistant Principal,
New York City Public Schools

Liz Sweeney, Elementary Math Department,
Boston Public Schools

Lucy West, Consultant, Metamorphosis:
Teaching Learning Communities, Inc.

This revision of the curriculum was built on the work of the many authors who contributed to the first edition (published between 1994 and 1998). We acknowledge the critical contributions of these authors in developing the content and pedagogy of *Investigations*:

Authors

Joan Akers

Michael T. Battista

Douglas H. Clements

Karen Economopoulos

Marlene Kliman

Jan Mokros

Megan Murray

Ricardo Nemirovsky

Andee Rubin

Susan Jo Russell

Cornelia Tierney

Contributing Authors

Mary Berle-Carman

Rebecca B. Corwin

Rebeka Eston

Claryce Evans

Anne Goodrow

Cliff Konold

Chris Mainhart

Sue McMillen

Jerrie Moffet

Tracy Noble

Kim O'Neil

Mark Ogonowski

Julie Sarama

Amy Shulman Weinberg

Margie Singer

Virginia Woolley

Tracey Wright

Contents

U N I T   5

Equal Groups

Investigations

Overview of Program Components

FOR TEACHERS

The **Curriculum Units** are the teaching guides. (See far right.)

Implementing Investigations in Grade 3 offers suggestions for implementing the curriculum. It also contains a comprehensive index.

The **Differentiation and Intervention Guide** offers additional activities for each Investigation to support the range of learners.

Investigations for the Interactive Whiteboard provides whole-class instructional support to enhance each session.

The **Resource Masters and Transparencies CD** contains all reproducible materials that support instruction. The **LogoPaths CD** provides an environment in which students investigate a variety of geometric ideas.

FOR STUDENTS

The **Student Activity Book** contains the consumable student pages (Recording Sheets, Homework, Practice, and so on).

The **Student Math Handbook** contains Math Words and Ideas pages and Games directions.

The *Investigations* Curriculum

Investigations in Number, Data, and Space® is a K–5 mathematics curriculum designed to engage students in making sense of mathematical ideas. Six major goals guided the development of the *Investigations in Number, Data, and Space*® curriculum. The curriculum is designed to:

- Support students to make sense of mathematics and learn that they can be mathematical thinkers

- Focus on computational fluency with whole numbers as a major goal of the elementary grades

- Provide substantive work in important areas of mathematics—rational numbers, geometry, measurement, data, and early algebra—and connections among them

- Emphasize reasoning about mathematical ideas

- Communicate mathematics content and pedagogy to teachers

- Engage the range of learners in understanding mathematics

Underlying these goals are three guiding principles that are touchstones for the *Investigations* team as we approach both students and teachers as agents of their own learning:

1. *Students have mathematical ideas.* Students come to school with ideas about numbers, shapes, measurements, patterns, and data. If given the opportunity to learn in an environment that stresses making sense of mathematics, students build on the ideas they already have and learn about new mathematics they have never encountered. Students learn that they are capable of having mathematical ideas, applying what they know to new situations, and thinking and reasoning about unfamiliar problems.

2. *Teachers are engaged in ongoing learning* about mathematics content, pedagogy, and student learning. The curriculum provides material for professional development, to be used by teachers individually or in groups, that supports teachers' continued learning as they use the curriculum over several years. The *Investigations* curriculum materials are designed as much to be a dialogue with teachers as to be a core of content for students.

3. *Teachers collaborate with the students and curriculum materials* to create the curriculum as enacted in the classroom. The only way for a good curriculum to be used well is for teachers to be active participants in implementing it. Teachers use the curriculum to maintain a clear, focused, and coherent agenda for mathematics teaching. At the same time, they observe and listen carefully to students, try to understand how they are thinking, and make teaching decisions based on these observations.

Investigations is based on experience from research and practice, including field testing that involved documentation of thousands of hours in classrooms, observations of students, input from teachers, and analysis of student work. As a result, the curriculum addresses the learning needs of real students in a wide range of classrooms and communities. The investigations are carefully designed to invite all students into mathematics—girls and boys; members of diverse cultural, ethnic, and language groups; and students with a wide variety of strengths, needs, and interests.

Based on this extensive classroom testing, the curriculum takes seriously the time students need to develop a strong conceptual foundation and skills based on that foundation. Each curriculum unit focuses on an area of content in depth, providing time for students to develop and practice ideas across a variety of activities and contexts that build on each other. Daily guidelines for time spent on class sessions, Classroom Routines (K–3), and Ten-Minute Math (3–5) reflect the commitment to devoting adequate time to mathematics in each school day.

About This Curriculum Unit

This **Curriculum Unit** is one of nine teaching guides in Grade 3. The fifth unit in Grade 3 is *Equal Groups*.

- The **Introduction and Overview** section organizes and presents the instructional materials, provides background information, and highlights important features specific to this unit.

- Each Curriculum Unit contains several **Investigations.** Each Investigation focuses on a set of related mathematical ideas.

- Investigations are divided into one-hour **Sessions,** or lessons.

- Sessions have a combination of these parts: **Activity, Discussion, Math Workshop, Assessment Activity,** and **Session Follow-Up.**

- Each session also has one or more **Classroom Routines** and **Ten-Minute Math** activities that are done outside of math time.

- At the back of the book is a collection of **Teacher Notes** and **Dialogue Boxes** that provide professional development related to the unit.

- Also included at the back of the book are the **Student Math Handbook** pages for this unit.

- The **Index** provides a way to look up important words or terms.

Overview

O F   T H I S   U N I T

Investigation	Session	Day	
INVESTIGATION 1 **Things That Come in Groups** Students make lists of things that come in groups. They illustrate multiplication situations and write equations to match.	**1.1** Many Things Come in Groups	1	
	1.2 How Many in Several Groups?	2	
	1.3 Solving Multiplication Problems	3	
	1.4 Assessment: Solving Problems About Our Pictures	4	
INVESTIGATION 2 **Skip Counting and 100 Charts** Students highlight multiples on 100 charts and discuss patterns and relationships. They use known multiplication combinations to solve more difficult ones.	**2.1** Highlighting Multiples on 100 Charts	5	
	2.2 More Multiples	6	
	2.3 Solving Related Story Problems	7	
	2.4 Patterns and Relationships	8	
	2.5 Assessment: Counting Around the Class	9	
	2.6 Using Multiplication Combinations	10	
INVESTIGATION 3 **Arrays** Students are introduced to arrays to represent multiplication. They use arrays to learn multiplication combinations with products up to 50 and to find factors of numbers up to 50.	**3.1** Arranging Chairs	11	
	3.2 Investigating Arrays	12	
	3.3 Finding the Number of Squares in an Array	13	
	3.4 Array Games—Part 1	14	
	3.5 Learning Multiplication Combinations	15	
	3.6 Array Games—Part 2	16	
INVESTIGATION 4 **Understanding Division** Students examine the inverse relationship between multiplication and division. They write story problems for a class multiplication and division book.	**4.1** Solving Division Problems	17	
	4.2 Multiply or Divide?	18	
	4.3 Writing Story Problems	19	
	4.4 Missing Factors	20	
	4.5 Solving Multiplication and Division Problems	21	
	4.6 Solving Multiplication and Division Problems, *continued*	22	
	4.7 End-of-Unit Assessment	23	

Each *Investigations* session has some combination of these five parts: **Activity, Discussion, Math Workshop, Assessment Activity,** and **Session Follow-Up.** These session parts are indicated in the chart below. Each session also has one **Classroom Routine or Ten-Minute Math** activity that is done outside of math time.

 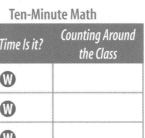

Ⓦ Interactive Whiteboard

Ten-Minute Math

Activity	Discussion	Math Workshop	Assessment Activity	Session Follow-Up
●●●				●
Ⓦ	Ⓦ			●
●Ⓦ●				●
	●		●	●
Ⓦ●				●
Ⓦ	Ⓦ			●
●	Ⓦ			●
Ⓦ	Ⓦ			●
	Ⓦ	●		●
	Ⓦ	●		●
Ⓦ●				●
Ⓦ	●			●
	Ⓦ	●		●
Ⓦ		●		●
Ⓦ	●			●
Ⓦ		●		●
●	Ⓦ			●
●	Ⓦ			●
Ⓦ●				●
Ⓦ●				●
	Ⓦ	●		●
	Ⓦ	●		●
			●	●

What Time Is it?	Counting Around the Class
Ⓦ	
Ⓦ	
Ⓦ	
Ⓦ	
	Ⓦ
	Ⓦ
	Ⓦ
	Ⓦ
	Ⓦ
	Ⓦ
Ⓦ	
Ⓦ	
Ⓦ	
	Ⓦ
	Ⓦ
	Ⓦ
Ⓦ	
Ⓦ	
Ⓦ	
Ⓦ	
Ⓦ	
Ⓦ	
Ⓦ	

Mathematics

Equal Groups is the third Grade 3 unit in the number and operations strand of *Investigations*. It begins the Grades 3 to 5 sequence of multiplication and division units. In these units, students investigate the properties of multiplication and division, examine the inverse relationship between these two operations, and develop strategies for solving multiplication and division problems.

LOOKING BACK During Grade 2, most students made the shift from working and counting primarily in ones, to working and counting by groups of ones. Students began to develop strategies for counting by equal groups. This work was set in contexts that encouraged counting by groups of 2, 5, or 10. Students found the number of legs or fingers in a group of people, used coin equivalencies to make trades, and represented quantities with tally marks. The work culminated in activities focused specifically on groups of ten and on the base-ten structure of our number system (i.e., 58 is made up of 5 tens and 8 ones). Students also began working with division situations as they solved problems about sharing a variety of objects equally and making equal-size groups.

This unit focuses on 5 Mathematical Emphases:

1 Whole Number Operations **Understanding the meaning of multiplication**

Math Focus Points

- Understanding multiplication as combining equal groups

- Writing and solving multiplication problems in context

- Identifying the number of groups, the number in each group, and the product in a multiplication situation

- Understanding the relationship among skip counting, repeated addition, and multiplication

- Using and understanding multiplication notation

At the beginning of this unit, student work focuses on developing the idea that multiplication involves some *number of equal-sized groups*. Students put this understanding into practice through writing and solving multiplication problems in familiar contexts. They examine and identify the three pieces of mathematical information in a multiplication situation—the number of groups, the size of each group, and the product. They are introduced to and learn to use multiplication notation.

> **Things That Come in 2s**
>
> eyes   shoes
>
> ears   mittens
>
> twins

As students solve problems in context, they develop their own strategies for doing multiplication and division. They learn that both operations involve equal groups. Multiplication is typically used when the size of each group and the number of groups is known and we want to find the product—the total number of items. Division is used when the total quantity is known and we want to find out either the number or the size of the groups.

2 Whole Number Operations **Reasoning about numbers and their factors and multiples**

Math Focus Points

- Finding the multiples of the numbers 2, 3, 4, 5, 6, and 10 by skip counting

- Describing and comparing characteristics of the multiples of a number

- Understanding that doubling (or halving) one factor in a multiplication expression doubles (or halves) the product

In Investigation 2, students determine, describe, and compare sets of multiples. As they highlight multiples of 2, 3, 4, 5, 6, and 10 on 100 charts, they become familiar with the multiples of these common numbers and notice their patterns and characteristics. The visual patterns on the 100 chart are intriguing to students (and helpful in highlighting the charts correctly with each set of multiples). However, it is when students compare sets of multiples that they are delving into important ideas about how multiplication works. For example, when they examine the multiples of 5 and of 10 together, they see that there are two multiples of 5 for each multiple of 10 on the chart; it takes three jumps of 10 to get to 30, but 6 jumps of 5.

1	2	3	4	5	6	7	8	9	10
11	12	13	14	15	16	17	18	19	20
21	22	23	24	25	26	27	28	29	30
31	32	33	34	35	36	37	38	39	40
41	42	43	44	45	46	47	48	49	50
51	52	53	54	55	56	57	58	59	60
61	62	63	64	65	66	67	68	69	70
71	72	73	74	75	76	77	78	79	80
81	82	83	84	85	86	87	88	89	90
91	92	93	94	95	96	97	98	99	100

Such observations lead to an investigation of how knowing the multiples of one number can help them determine multiples of a number that is double or half that number: how can a student use the known product of 4×3 to help solve 6×3? Students develop representations to support their arguments that multiplying a number by 3 results in a product half as large as multiplying the same number by 6.

3 Whole Number Operations Understanding and working with an array model of multiplication

Math Focus Points

◆ Using arrays to model multiplication situations

◆ Using arrays to find factors of 2-digit numbers up to 50

◆ Using arrays to identify characteristics of numbers, including prime and square numbers

◆ Using arrays to find a product by skip counting by one of its dimensions

◆ Breaking an array into parts to find the product represented by the array

Students continue to develop visual images that support their understandings of multiplication and division as they are introduced to arrays—rectangular arrangements of objects in rows and columns.

Sample Student Work

Students use rectangular arrays to represent the relationship between a product and its factors: the number of squares in the array represents the product, and the length and width of the rectangle are one pair of factors of that product.

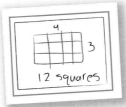

Sample Student Work

Through using an array model, students begin to visualize important multiplication relationships. They see, for example, that the solution to 3×6 is the same as the solution to 6×3, which leads to the development of the commutative property of multiplication.

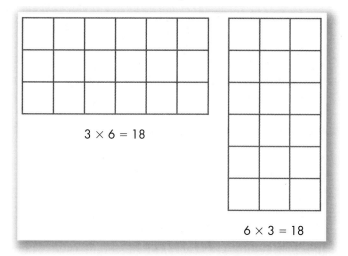

$3 \times 6 = 18$

$6 \times 3 = 18$

As they work on solving multiplication problems, they use arrays to visualize ways of breaking problems apart $[7 \times 6 = (5 \times 6) + (2 \times 6)]$ that lead to developing understanding of the distributive property of multiplication. Students consider features of numbers (including prime and square numbers) by examining the shapes of arrays. The use of arrays in this unit supports a number of ideas that are essential for students' understanding of how multiplication and division work, as well as for their development of computational fluency.

4 Computational Fluency Learning the multiplication combinations with products up to 50 fluently

Math Focus Points

- Using known multiplication combinations to determine the product of more difficult combinations

- Identifying and learning multiplication combinations not yet known

Throughout this unit, as students develop their own multiplication and division strategies, they are aided by knowing many of the single-digit multiplication combinations. Although we do not expect them to know all of the multiplication combinations by the end of this unit, it is our expectation that students will complete Grade 3 with a good grasp of the multiplication combinations with products up to 50. Through their work with skip counting and arrays, they will also develop ways to solve other problems quickly; for example, they will learn to use a known answer to find an unknown one ("8×9 is like 4×9 twice, so it's 36 and 36, and that's 72," or "9×6 is equal to 10×6 minus one 6. That's $60 - 6$, so the answer is 54.")

5 Whole Number Operations Developing strategies for division based on understanding the inverse relationship between multiplication and division

Math Focus Points

- Understanding division as the splitting of a quantity into equal groups

- Using the inverse relationship between multiplication and division to solve problems

- Using multiplication combinations to solve division problems

- Using and understanding division notation

- Writing and solving division problems in context

Although students encounter division situations in each of the first three investigations, it is in Investigation 4 that students are formally introduced to division and division notation. Their work in this investigation develops their understanding of division as the splitting of a quantity into equal groups of a particular number, or splitting a quantity into a particular number of equal groups.

In order to solve division problems, students must recognize different division situations. There are two kinds of situations to consider: those that involve *sharing* ("Divide 35 pennies among five people equally; how many pennies are in each share?"), and those that involve *grouping* ("How many groups of five pennies can I make if I have 35 pennies?"). Students learn to recognize what information is given in each type of problem and what they must figure out.

Third graders approach most division problems by using multiplication. For example, to find how many groups of five pennies can be made from 35 pennies, some students might count by 5s to find the number of groups. Others might use reasoning based on what they know.

I know that five 5s is 25.
And two more 5s make 35.
So I have 7 groups of 5.

Sample Student Work

The students' work looks like multiplication even though they are solving a division problem. These students are using their knowledge of the relationship between division and multiplication.

Students are introduced to two forms of division notation: $35 \div 5$ and $5\overline{)35}$. Students also learn how to interpret the numbers and symbols in terms of the meaning and actions of division.

Ten-Minute Math activities focus on

◈ Telling time to any minute on a digital or analog clock

◈ Determining intervals of time to the minute

◈ Finding the multiples of numbers through skip counting

◈ Becoming familiar with multiplication patterns

◈ Understanding the relationship between skip counting and multiplication

LOOKING FORWARD

Students are assessed on their fluency with multiplication combinations up to a product of 50 later in Grade 3 in the unit *How Many Hundreds? How Many Miles?* and then on all the combinations up to 12×12 in Grade 4. Students continue to develop strategies for solving multiplication and division problems in three units in Grade 4. They further develop their understanding of the distributive property of multiplication and apply this understanding to the solving of 2-digit multiplication problems. They complete learning the multiplication combinations to 12×12 and work on their counterparts for division. They investigate the effect on the product of multiplying one factor by 10 or a multiple of 10 and of doubling and halving one factor. They continue their work with division and extend it to include problems that result in a remainder. Later they apply their strategies to multiplication and division problems with larger numbers and develop methods of keeping track of all the parts of a problem that involve multidigit numbers. In Grade 5, students consolidate their strategies for both multiplication and division while they continue to explore the properties of both operations.

Technology Note

Using the *LogoPaths* Software Students were formally introduced to the *LogoPaths* software in the 2-D Geometry and Measurement unit, *Perimeter, Angles, and Area,* the fourth unit in the Grade 3 sequence. We recommend that students continue to have access to the software **outside of math time** in order to return to *Feed the Turtle,* a *LogoPaths* activity, and to spend time with the *Free Explore* option. For information about the *LogoPaths* software and directions for *Feed the Turtle,* refer to the *Software Support Reference Guide* found on the CD. See **Part 5: Technology in *Investigations*** in *Implementing Investigations in Grade 3:* Introducing and Managing the *LogoPaths* Software in Grade 3.

Assessment

IN THIS UNIT

ONGOING ASSESSMENT: Observing Students at Work

The following sessions provide **Ongoing Assessment: Observing Students at Work** opportunities:

- **Session 1.1, pp. 26 and 27**
- **Session 1.2, pp. 30 and 33**
- **Session 1.3, p. 37**
- **Session 1.4, p. 41**
- **Session 2.1, pp. 50 and 52**
- **Session 2.2, p. 57**
- **Session 2.3, p. 62**

- **Session 2.4, p. 69**
- **Session 2.5, p. 74**
- **Session 3.1, p. 85**
- **Session 3.2, p. 90**
- **Session 3.4, p. 99**
- **Session 3.5, p. 105**
- **Session 3.6, p. 109**

- **Session 4.1, p. 118**
- **Session 4.2, p. 122**
- **Session 4.3, p. 127**
- **Session 4.4, p. 131**
- **Session 4.5, p. 136**
- **Session 4.7, p. 142**

WRITING OPPORTUNITIES

The following sessions have **writing** opportunities for students to explain their mathematical thinking:

- **Session 1.2, p. 33**
  Student Activity Book, p. 3

- **Session 2.3, p. 61**
  Student Activity Book, p. 16

- **Session 2.5, p. 75**
  Student Activity Book, p. 24

- **Session 3.4, p. 100**
  Student Activity Book, p. 33

- **Session 4.3, p. 126**
  Writing Problems for the Class Book

PORTFOLIO OPPORTUNITIES

The following sessions have work appropriate for a **portfolio:**

- **Session 1.2, p. 33**
  M6, Pictures of Things That Come in Groups

- **Session 2.3, p. 60**
  Student Activity Book, p. 14

- **Session 2.5, p. 74**
  M13, Assessment: *Counting Around the Class*

- **Session 3.4, p. 98**
  Student Activity Book, p. 31

- **Session 4.2, p. 122**
  Student Activity Book, p. 42

- **Session 4.7, p. 142**
  M44, End-of-Unit Assessment

Assessing the Benchmarks

Observing students as they engage in conversation about their ideas is a primary means to assess their mathematical understanding. Consider all of your students' work, not just the written assessments. See the chart below for suggestions about key activities to observe.

See the **Differentiation and Intervention Guide** for quizzes that can be used after each Investigation.

Benchmarks in This Unit	Key Activities to Observe	Assessment
1. Demonstrate an understanding of multiplication and division as involving groups of equal groups.	**Session 1.2:** Pictures of Things That Come in Groups **Session 1.2:** Writing "Groups of" as Multiplication	**Session 1.4 Assessment Activity:** Solving Problems About Our Pictures **Session 4.7 End-of-Unit Assessment:** Problems 1A, 1B, and 2
2. Solve multiplication combinations and related division problems by using skip counting or known multiplication combinations.	*Counting Around the Class* **(Ten-Minute Math)** **Session 2.2:** Relationships Between the Multiples of 5 and 10 **Session 2.2:** Highlighting the Multiples of 3 and 6	**Session 2.5 Assessment Activity:** *Counting Around the Class* **Session 4.7 End-of-Unit Assessment:** Problems 1A, 1B, and 2
3. Interpret and use multiplication and division notation.	**Session 3.1:** Arranging Chairs **Session 4.2:** Multiply or Divide?	**Session 1.4 Assessment Activity:** Solving Problems About Our Pictures **Session 4.7 End-of-Unit Assessment:** Problems 1A, 1B, and 2
4. Demonstrate fluency with multiplication combinations with products up to 50 (by the end of Grade 3).	**Session 3.5:** Using Known Multiplication Combinations **Session 3.5:** Making Multiplication Cards	To be assessed in Unit 8, Operations 4

Relating the Mathematical Emphases to the Benchmarks

Mathematical Emphases	Benchmarks
Whole-Number Operations Understanding the meaning of multiplication	1, 2, and 3
Whole-Number Operations Reasoning about numbers and their factors and multiples	1, 2, and 3
Whole-Number Operations Understanding and working with an array model of multiplication	2, 3, and 4
Computational Fluency Learning the multiplication combinations with products up to 50 fluently	4
Whole-Number Operations Developing strategies for division based on understanding the inverse relationship between multiplication and division	1, 2, and 3

Algebra Connections

In this unit, your students will have opportunities to engage with ideas that lay a foundation for algebra. Eight- and nine-year-olds can and do think algebraically. Part of the work of Grade 3 is helping students learn to verbalize and represent those thoughts. Such skills will provide the basis for making sense of algebraic notation when it is introduced in the future.

Using Properties of Multiplication

Consider the following vignette, in which a teacher asks students to explain how they figured out 9×4:

Philip: I know that 5×4 is 20 and 4×4 is 16. $20 + 16$ is 36, so 9×4 is 36.

Elena: First I think of 10×4. I know that is 40. I want 9 of the 4s so I have to take away one 4. $40 - 4 = 36$.

Jung: I know 9×2, that's 18. Then I double that to get $9 \times 4 = 36$. I like to double.

Kenji: I know all my 4s. 4×9 is the same as 9×4. They are both 36.

In this unit, when given a multiplication combination that they did not know, students are encouraged to build up to the answer by beginning with a part of the problem that they did know. Philip broke 9 into $5 + 4$ and then added two combinations he knows $(5 \times 4) + (4 \times 4)$ to figure out $9 \times 4 = 36$. Elena's approach is similar to Philip's. She saw that 9 can be considered as $10 - 1$ and then subtracted two combinations she knows $(10 \times 4) - (1 \times 4)$ to get $9 \times 4 = 36$. When Jung wanted to figure out 9×4, she began with $9 \times 2 = 18$. She realized this is exactly half of the answer and so she doubled 18 to get 36. Kenji realized that if he knows 4×9, he also knows 9×4.

The work of these students illustrates important properties of multiplication. Philip and Elena both use the distributive property; for Philip it is $(5 \times 4) + (4 \times 4) = 9 \times 4$ and for Elena, $10 \times 4 = (9 \times 4) + (1 \times 4)$. Written in more general and more formal algebraic terms, the distributive property is expressed as $(a \times c) + (b \times c) = (a + b) \times c$. Jung calls upon the associative property; that is, the structure of Jung's approach is to say $9 \times 4 = 9 \times (2 \times 2) = (9 \times 2) \times 2 = 18 \times 2 = 36$. Expressed in general terms, the associative property is $a \times (b \times c) = (a \times b) \times c$. Kenji is using the commutative property: $a \times b = b \times a$.

In this unit, students develop a sense of how multiplication works by using a variety of representations, such as skip counting, story contexts, arrays, and drawings of multiplicative situations. In the context of performing calculations and learning factor combinations, students use the properties implicitly by focusing on ways to count groups of objects. This work lays the foundation for understanding these three properties of multiplication.

Also in this unit, students work to articulate and explain how and why the commutative property works by calling upon their models. The associative and distributive properties will be examined in more detail in Grades 4 and 5.

Understanding the Inverse Relationship Between Division and Multiplication

Just as many students and adults solve subtraction problems by using an addition strategy, students often solve division problems by using a multiplication strategy.

Consider this vignette:

Kathryn and Adam are working on the following problem:

There are 28 desks in the classroom. The teacher puts them in groups of four. How many groups of desks are in the classroom?

Kathryn: I am picturing the desks in groups of four and counting by 4s: 4, 8, 12, 16, 20, 24, 28. That means I have seven groups of four desks to make 28.

Adam: I know that five groups of four would be 20. This is two more groups of 4 and so it is 20 + 8, or 28.

In this vignette, Kathryn and Adam are using what they know about multiplication to solve a division problem. Kathryn uses counting by 4s, and Adam uses the distributive property of multiplication. Both students use grouping by 4s in their approaches. The fact that these students can interpret their multiplication strategies to correctly answer a division problem is based on the inverse relationship between multiplication and division. Since $7 \times 4 = 28$, then $28 \div 4 = 7$ or, in more general terms, if $a \times b = c$, then $c \div b = a$.

In this unit, students solve story problems to develop a meaning of the operation of division. They draw upon their multiplication combinations and strategies to solve the division problems. As they work, encourage students to articulate their reasoning by asking questions such as the following:

- Why is it that a strategy using multiplication solves this division problem?

- How is counting by 4s related to the original problem?

- What part of the original problem have you solved when you write 5×4?

- What else do you need to do to complete the problem?

Student responses to such questions will help them articulate and clarify their own thinking about the relationship between multiplication and division. Their responses also support the development of mental images to represent the operations and will form the basis for future work examining these operations and their properties.

Investigations students are encouraged to verbalize the generalizations they see about numbers and operations, and to explain and justify them using materials and tools, such as cubes or diagrams. For most adults, notation, such as variables, operation signs, and equal signs, is the chief identifying feature of algebra. The notation, however, expresses rules about how operations work that students can reason out for themselves. This *reasoning*—about how numbers can be put together and taken apart under different operations—not the notation, is the work of elementary students in algebra.

Note: In the text for the sessions, you will find Algebra Notes that identify where these early algebra discussions are likely to arise. Some of the **Teacher Notes** and **Dialogue Boxes** further elaborate the ideas and illustrate students' conversations about them.

IN THIS UNIT

The **Classroom Routines** and **Ten-Minute Math** activities, to be done in ten minutes outside of math class, are introduced in a unit and repeated throughout the grade. Specific directions for the day's activity are provided in each session. For the full description and variations of the Classroom Routines and Ten-Minute Math activities, see *Implementing Investigations in Grade 3.*

Activity	Introduced	Full Description of Activity and Its Variations
Classroom Routine: *What's the Temperature?*	Unit 1, Session 1.1	*Implementing Investigations in Grade 3*
Ten-Minute Math: *What Time Is It?*	Unit 3, Session 3.1	*Implementing Investigations in Grade 3*
Ten-Minute Math: *Counting Around the Class*	Unit 5, Session 1.3 (this unit)	*Implementing Investigations in Grade 3*

What's the Temperature?

Students record the outside temperature every Wednesday morning on a chart and on a graph. This data set will be used in the unit *Stories, Tables, and Graphs,* when students describe changes in temperature over time.

Math Focus Points

◆ Learning about temperature: reading a thermometer, learning to associate different temperatures with words colder and warmer, and establishing landmark temperatures

◆ Recording information in a table and on a graph

◆ Reading information from the shape of a graph, for example, hot cold, increasing, decreasing

What Time Is It?

Students practice naming, notating, telling, and setting time to the minute on analog and digital clocks. They predict ending times when given intervals and the starting times of activities, and share strategies based on numerical reasoning about what time they think it will be. They also determine the length of various amounts of time.

Math Focus Points

◆ Telling time to any minute on a digital or analog clock

◆ Determining intervals of time to the minute

Counting Around the Class

Students count around the class by a particular number. Before the count starts, they estimate the ending number of the count and the number the last person in the class will say. Students discuss relationships between the chosen factor and its multiples.

Math Focus Points

◆ Finding the multiples of numbers through skip counting

◆ Becoming familiar with multiplication patterns

◆ Understanding the relationship between skip counting and multiplication

Practice and Review

IN THIS UNIT

Practice and review play a critical role in the *Investigations* program. The following components and features are available to provide regular reinforcement of key mathematical concepts and procedures.

Books	Features	In This Unit . . .
Curriculum Unit	**The Classroom Routines** and **Ten-Minute Math** activities, to be done in ten minutes outside of math class, are introduced in a unit and repeated throughout the grade. Specific directions for the day's activity are provided in each session. For the full description and variations of the Classroom Routines and Ten-Minute Math activities, see *Implementing Investigations in Grade 3*.	• **All sessions**
Student Activity Book	**Daily Practice** pages in the *Student Activity Book* provide one of three types of written practice: **reinforcement** of the content of the unit, **ongoing review,** or **enrichment** opportunities. Some Daily Practice pages will also have Ongoing Review items with multiple-choice problems similar to those on standardized tests.	• **All sessions**
	Homework pages in the *Student Activity Book* are an extension of the work done in class. At times they help students prepare for upcoming activities.	• **Session 1.1** • **Session 3.4** • **Session 1.2** • **Session 3.5** • **Session 1.4** • **Session 3.6** • **Session 2.1** • **Session 4.1** • **Session 2.3** • **Session 4.2** • **Session 2.5** • **Session 4.3** • **Session 3.3**
Student Math Handbook	**Math Words and Ideas** in the *Student Math Handbook* are pages that summarize key words and ideas. Most Words and Ideas pages have at least one exercise.	• **Student Math Handbook, pp. 39–55**
	Games pages are found in a section of the *Student Math Handbook*.	• **Student Math Handbook, pp. G9, G10, G17–G18, G19–G20**

Differentiation

Supporting the Range of Learners

The **Differentiation and Intervention Guide** provides Intervention, Extension, and Practice activities for use within each Investigation.

Sessions	1.1	1.2	1.3	1.4	2.1	2.2	2.3	2.4	3.1	3.2	3.3	3.4	3.5	4.1	4.3	4.4	4.5	4.7
Intervention			●	●	●	●	●	●	●			●	●	●	●	●	●	●
Extension		●		●				●	●		●					●		
ELL	●			●								●			●	●		

Intervention

Suggestions are made to support and engage students who are having difficulty with a particular idea, activity, or problem.

Extension

Suggestions are made to support and engage students who finish early or may be ready for additional challenge.

English Language Learners (ELL)

In this unit, students learn to visualize the operations of multiplication and division and apply these operations to real-life situations and story contexts. Students develop strategies to make multiplication easier, such as using smaller, known multiplication combinations to solve more difficult problems. Cubes, skip-counting charts, array cards, and drawings provide visual images of multiplication, the relationships among factors and multiples of numbers, and the inverse relationship between multiplication and division. Review relevant vocabulary in context and encourage English Language Learners to use cubes, skip counting charts, arrays, and drawings to model and discuss their ideas.

Encourage English Language Learners to exchange ideas with you and with smaller groups of students. Some will feel more comfortable writing down their words before being asked to say them aloud. Others might need you to provide the language for what they are doing. "I see you've taken the cubes and made an *array* of 5 x 7. Your array has 5 *rows* with 7 cubes in each *row*. Show me how you can figure out how many cubes are in the 5 x 7 array. So, you *skip counted* by 5s to find the *product*." Then ask the students to restate what you've said or to explain the next problem: "What will you do for this one? Yes, you can use your cubes to make an *array* of six *rows* with seven cubes in each *row*. The *product* of the 5 x 7 array was 35. Can that help you find the *product* of the 6 x 7 array?"

For relating multiplication and division situations to story contexts, students may need to draw their story idea first and then get help putting it into words. For pages of story problems, recognize that English Language Learners may understand the math but have difficulty with the language of the story. Help them by reading problems aloud, sketching objects, and modeling actions as needed.

Working with the Range of Learners: Classroom Cases is a set of episodes written by teachers that focuses on meeting the needs of the range of learners in the classroom. In the first section, *Setting up the Mathematical Community,* teachers write about how they create a supportive and productive learning environment in their classrooms. In the next section, *Accommodations for Learning,* teachers focus on specific modifications they make to meet the needs of some of their learners. In the last section, *Language and Representation,* teachers share how they help students use representations and develop language to investigate and express mathematical ideas. The questions at the end of each case provide a starting point for your own reflection or for discussion with colleagues. See *Implementing Investigations in Grade 3* for this set of episodes.

Mathematical Emphasis

Whole Number Operations Understanding the meaning of multiplication

Math Focus Points

◆ Understanding multiplication as combining equal groups

◆ Writing and solving multiplication problems in context

◆ Identifying the number of groups, the number in each group, and the product in a multiplication situation

◆ Understanding the relationship among skip counting, repeated addition, and multiplication

◆ Using and understanding multiplication notation

Things That Come in Groups

	Student Activity Book	Student Math Handbook	Professional Development: Read Ahead of Time	
SESSION 1.1 p. 24				
Many Things Come in Groups Students make lists of things that come in groups of 2 to 12 and use the lists to create multiplication situations. They solve teacher- and class-generated multiplication problems.	1–2	39, 40–41	• **Mathematics in This Unit,** p. 10 • **Teacher Note:** Images of Multiplication, p. 145 • **Part 4: Ten-Minute Math and Classroom Routines** in *Implementing Investigations in Grade 3*: What's the Temperature?	
SESSION 1.2 p. 28				
How Many in Several Groups? Students illustrate multiplication situations and write sentences describing the number of groups, the number in each group, and the product. They write multiplication equations to match their illustrations.	3	39, 40–41, 42	• **Part 4: Ten-Minute Math and Classroom Routines** in *Implementing Investigations in Grade 3*: What Time Is It?	
SESSION 1.3 p. 34				
Solving Multiplication Problems Students are introduced to the Ten-Minute Math activity *Counting Around the Class*. They solve problems about multiplication situations.	4–7	39, 40–41	• **Part 4: Ten-Minute Math and Classroom Routines** in *Implementing investigations in Grade 3*: Counting Around the Class	
SESSION 1.4 p. 39				
Assessment: Solving Problems About Our Pictures Students illustrate multiplication situations and solve problems about their pictures as an assessment of their understanding of the meaning of multiplication.	8–9	39, 40–41, 42	• **Teacher Note:** Assessement: Solving Problems About Our Pictures, p. 149	

Classroom Routines and Ten-Minute Math

See page 18 for an overview.

What's the Temperature?	*What Time Is It?*
• Mount the thermometer outside the classroom window.	• Demonstration clock
• Post the Date and Temperature chart and the Temperature graph in the classroom.	• Student clocks (1 per pair)

Materials to Gather	Materials to Prepare
• **Connecting cubes** (50 per pair; as needed)	• **M7–M8, Family Letter** Make copies. (1 per student) • **Construction paper 11″ x 17″** Label 11 sheets, with one label on each sheet: "Things That Come in 2s", "Things That Come in 3s", and so on to "Things That Come in 12s".
• **Class lists of "Things That Come in Groups"** (from Session 1.1) • **Colored pencils, markers, or crayons** (1 per student) • **Unlined paper** (4 sheets per student)	• **M6, Pictures of Things That Come in Groups** Make copies. (2 per student) • **M9–M10, Family Letter** Make copies. (1 per student) • **Chart paper** Draw four 5-pointed stars at the top of the chart paper.
• **T60, Multiplication Chart** 🖵 • **Chart paper** • **Connecting cubes** (40 per student)	
• **Class lists of "Things That Come in Groups"** (from Session 1.1) • **Unlined paper** (2 sheets per student) • **Colored pencils, markers, or crayons** (1 per student)	

🖵 Overhead Transparency

Many Things Come in Groups

Math Focus Points

◆ Understanding multiplication as combining equal groups

◆ Writing and solving multiplication problems in context

Vocabulary

multiplication

Today's Plan		Materials
ACTIVITY **①** **Naming Things That Come in Groups**	20 MIN CLASS	• Construction paper*
ACTIVITY **②** **Asking Multiplication Questions**	20 MIN CLASS PAIRS	• Connecting cubes (as needed)
ACTIVITY **③** **Brainstorming About Groups**	20 MIN PAIRS	
SESSION FOLLOW-UP **④** **Daily Practice and Homework**		• *Student Activity Book*, pp. 1–2 • M7–M8, *Family Letter** • *Student Math Handbook*, pp. 39, 40–41

*See *Materials To Prepare,* p. 23.

Ten-Minute Math

What Time is It? What Time Will it Be? Show 10:15 on the demonstration clock.

What time is it on this clock?

If you start reading your book at this time and you read for 20 minutes, what time will it be when you stop reading?

In pairs, students share ideas about what time they think it will be. As a class, focus on counting by 5s from 10:15 to 10:35. Ask students a similar question using 1:40 as the starting time and 25 minutes for duration.

ACTIVITY

1 Naming Things That Come in Groups

20 MIN   CLASS

For the next few weeks we are going to be learning about multiplication and division. Both of these operations have to do with equal groups. Things like pencils, paper clips, hotdogs, and eggs are sold in groups. Things like petals on a flower and legs on a cat come in certain numbers. What things can you think of that come in equal groups?

Start a class list of things that come in groups on separate sheets of chart paper for each number from 2 to 12. Under each number record a few of the students' ideas.

Things That Come in 2s	Things That Come in 3s	Things That Come in 4s
ears	juice boxes	legs on a dog
eyes	leaves on a clover	quarters in a dollar
mittens	sides of a triangle	seasons in a year
shoes		
twins		

On each list, leave space to add new ideas or examples. Post the lists in numerical order where students can see them.

ACTIVITY

2 Asking Multiplication Questions

20 MIN   CLASS   PAIRS

To help students become familiar with situations for which multiplication can be used, pose two questions that can be solved by using multiplication. Base your questions on items from the class list.

We agree that there are usually five toes on a person's foot. How many toes would there be on four feet? There are four quarters in a dollar. How many quarters are there in three dollars?

Elicit student responses to these questions, being sure to ask students to share how they came up with their answers. Listen for strategies that demonstrate an understanding of these problems as containing groups of equal amounts (e.g., skip counting or repeated addition). Choose another

Professional Development

❶ **Teacher Note:** Images of Multiplication, p. 145

Differentiation

❷ **English Language Learners** This activity may generate a lot of new vocabulary for English Language Learners. You can help by previewing the question with them and helping them generate some initial examples. If English Language Learners have trouble expressing their ideas in English, ask them to sketch their examples and then help them put these examples into words. When you work with the full class, you can draw quick sketches of the examples other students give, and then have English Language Learners make a "Things That Come in Groups" picture dictionary.

item from the class lists and ask students to think of questions about several groups of that item. Work together as a class to come up with two questions.

> We agree that juice boxes often come in packages of three. People often buy more than one package at a time. What question can we ask about more than one package of juice boxes? What question can we ask about a different number of packages?

After the class has come up with two questions, students work in pairs to solve them. Circulate as students are working. Some students may benefit by representing the situations described in the multiplication problems with drawings or by using cubes or other counters to model the action of the problem.

ONGOING ASSESSMENT: Observing Students at Work

Students solve class-generated multiplication problems.

- **What strategies are students using to solve these problems?**
  Are they using counting by 1s, repeated addition, or skip counting?

ACTIVITY

20 MIN PAIRS

3 Brainstorming About Groups

Have students work in pairs for about 15 minutes.

Working with partners, students brainstorm more things that come in groups of 2 to 12.

In the last five minutes of the session, bring students together to add the new ideas to the class lists and to talk about any observations they might have about them.

What are the most common numbers that things are grouped in? Which numbers were hard to find? Why do you think some numbers occur more often than others?

Challenge students to think of something for every one of the numbers from 2 to 12 over the next few days. Save the class lists of "Things That Come in Groups" for use in the next session.

ONGOING ASSESSMENT: Observing Students at Work

Students generate additional examples of things that come in groups of 2 through 12.

- **Do students' ideas demonstrate an understanding of the concept of equal groups?**

SESSION FOLLOW-UP

4 Daily Practice and Homework

 Daily Practice: For reinforcement of this unit's content, have students complete *Student Activity Book* page 1.

Homework: Students talk with people at home about things that come in groups. They list new things they think of or find, either at home or at a store, writing the name and number per group of each item on *Student Activity Book* page 2. Remind students to return this homework before the next math session.

Student Math Handbook: Students and families may use *Student Math Handbook* pages 39, 40–41 for reference and review. See pages 176–181 in the back of this unit.

Family Letter: Send home copies of the Family Letter (M7–M8).

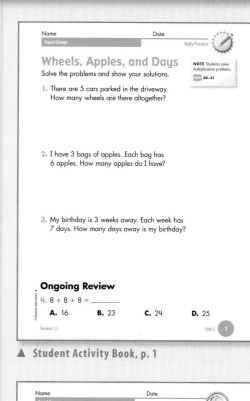

▲ **Student Activity Book, p. 1**

▲ **Student Activity Book, p. 2**

How Many in Several Groups?

Math Focus Points

◆ Understanding multiplication as combining equal groups

◆ Identifying the number of groups, the number in each group, and the product in a multiplication situation

◆ Understanding the relationship among skip counting, repeated addition, and multiplication

◆ Using and understanding multiplication notation

Vocabulary

equation

Today's Plan		Materials
ACTIVITY **① Pictures of Things That Come in Groups**	40 MIN CLASS INDIVIDUALS	• Class lists: "Things That Come in Groups" (from Session 1.1) • Colored pencils, markers, or crayons; unlined paper
DISCUSSION **② Writing "Groups of" as Multiplication**	20 MIN CLASS	• Chart paper*
SESSION FOLLOW-UP **③ Daily Practice and Homework**		• *Student Activity Book,* p. 3 • M6*; M9–M10, Family Letter* • *Student Math Handbook,* pp. 39, 40–41, 42

*See *Materials To Prepare*, p. 23.

Ten-Minute Math

What Time Is It? What Time Will It Be? Show 1:10 on the demonstration clock.

What time is it on this clock?

If I leave my house at 1:10 and come back 30 minutes later, what time will it be?

In pairs, students share ideas about what time they think it will be. As a class, focus on counting 30 by 5s from 1:10 to 1:40. Also collect strategies based on numerical reasoning such as: "I know that 10 + 30 = 40 so it would be 1:40." Ask students a similar question using 3:30 as the starting time and 20 minutes for duration.

40 MIN   CLASS   INDIVIDUALS

① Pictures of Things That Come in Groups

Take a few minutes to add to the class lists any new items that students discovered for homework. Focus on the lists on which there are only a few items.

Students now work on illustrating and labeling a drawing of their own based on the items on the list. Explain to students how this will work.

• You will assign a number to each student to work with (e.g., 4).

• Students choose an item from the list of things that come in that number and draw several of those items.

• Students write three sentences that tell how many groups, how many in each group, and how many in all.

Students' work should look like the following:

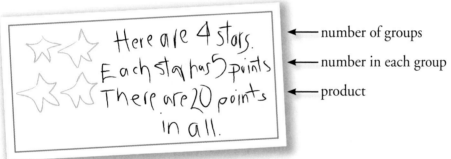

Here are 4 stars. ← number of groups
Each star has 5 points ← number in each group
There are 20 points ← product
in all.

Sample Student Work

Have students make several different pictures of groups, with each picture showing a different number of groups. For example, a student assigned the number 3 might draw four storybooks of "The Three Bears," two triangles with three sides each, and five three-leaf clovers. Suggest that students start with no more than six groups. They can illustrate more groups later.

Some teachers find it helpful to provide students with a template of the three sentences. You can write them on the board or on a sheet of chart paper or make copies and pass them out.

Here are ____.

Each ____ has ____.

There are ____ in all.

ONGOING ASSESSMENT: Observing Students at Work

Students illustrate multiplication situations and write three sentences stating the number of groups in their pictures, the number in each group, and the product.

- **Are students able to recognize and write sentences about the mathematical information contained in the situations they illustrated?**

- **How are students finding the products in their multiplication situations?**

DIFFERENTIATION: Supporting the Range of Learners

Think about which numbers to assign to which students, given your knowledge of the appropriate level of challenge for each student, keeping the numbers small for some students while challenging others with larger numbers.

Extension Assign higher numbers or encourage more than six groups to students who demonstrate that they are ready.

DISCUSSION

Writing "Groups of" as Multiplication

20 MIN   CLASS

Math Focus Points for Discussion

◈ Understanding the relationship among skip counting, repeated addition, and multiplication

◈ Using and understanding multiplication notation

Use students' pictures to introduce symbolic notation for multiplication. Ask a few students to share their strategies for finding the product in their multiplication situations. It is likely that many students will have used skip counting, repeated addition, or a combination of the two.

We can describe the problems on your pictures by using addition, and in fact, many of you used addition to figure out the total in your pictures. For example, Becky showed how she figured out that four stars have $5 + 5 + 5 + 5 = 20$ points.

Write the addition equation on the board. Ask students how many 5s they see in this equation and ask a student volunteer to point out the groups of five in the illustration of four stars.

Some of you skip counted to find the answer: 5, 10, 15, 20. How many times did you skip count by 5 to figure out the number of points in all? How is this similar to using repeated addition to solve the problem?

Students should recognize that both strategies involve four groups of 5. Now, introduce multiplication notation.❶

We can also write four groups of 5 as a multiplication equation: $4 \times 5 = 20$.❷

Write $4 \times 5 = 20$ on the board as well as on your illustration of the four stars.

Here are 4 stars.
Each star has 5 points.
There are 20 points in all.
$4 \times 5 = 20$

Math Notes

❶ **Standard Notation for Multiplication** It is important that your students learn to recognize, interpret, and use the standard notation for multiplication, both vertically and horizontally. Your challenge is to introduce notation in a way that allows students to interpret it meaningfully and use their knowledge of numbers and number relationships to solve problems, no matter what form of notation is used. For multiplication, students need to know that the vertical notation of a multiplication expression does not imply or dictate a particular procedure, such as the "carrying" algorithm. Keep the emphasis on understanding the problem context and using good number sense to solve the problem.

❷ **Is it 4 × 5 or 5 × 4?** *Investigations* has opted to use 4 groups of 5 as 4 × 5 in this curriculum. However, it is not necessary for students to follow this system rigidly. When students suggest a multiplication expression for a multiplication situation, what is important is that they understand what the numbers mean. For example, in the picture of 4 stars with 5 points each, students need to understand that the 4 represents the number of groups and that the 5 represents the number in each group, whether they notate this situation as 4 × 5 or 5 × 4.

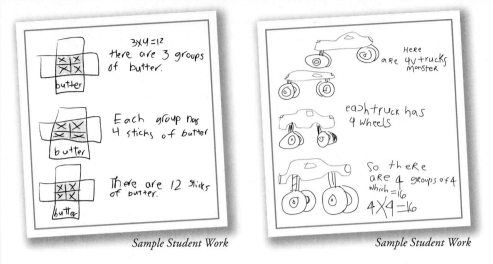

Sample Student Work   *Sample Student Work*

Ask a few volunteers to share their pictures. Have each student show a picture and read aloud the sentences that describe it. Other students then tell how to write the addition equation and corresponding multiplication equation for the problem. (If some students skip counted to find the product, add the skip counting sequence as well.) Write some of their examples on the board.

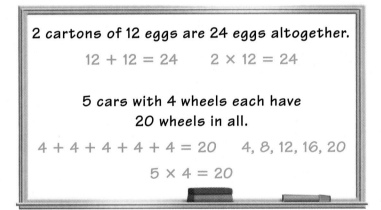

Help students connect the number of addends or the number of skip counts with the groups in the multiplication equations. For example, the two 12s in the addition equation represent the two groups of 12 eggs.

Students now decide what multiplication equation goes with each of the pictures they made and write them on their pictures.

If there is time, students can make additional pictures that show items from the lists of things that come in groups. Remind students to write the three important pieces of mathematical information and a multiplication equation to describe each picture.

Be sure to save the completed pictures for use in the next sessions. Also save the class lists of "Things That Come in Groups" for use in Investigation 4.

ONGOING ASSESSMENT: Observing Students at Work

Students write multiplication equations that represent the multiplication situations in their pictures of things that come in groups.

- **Are students correctly using multiplication notation to represent the information in their illustrations?**

DIFFERENTIATION: Supporting the Range of Learners

Extension Some students may be ready to make pictures with more than six groups.

SESSION FOLLOW-UP

3 Daily Practice and Homework

Daily Practice: For reinforcement of this unit's content, have students complete *Student Activity Book* page 3.

Homework: Students make more pictures like the ones they drew in class on two copies of Pictures of Things That Come in Groups (M6). Students describe each picture, both in words (being sure to include the three important pieces of information) and with a multiplication equation. Remind students to return this homework before the next math session.

Student Math Handbook: Students and families may use *Student Math Handbook* pages 39, 40–41, 42 for reference and review. See pages 176–181 in the back of this unit.

Family Letter: Send home copies of the Family Letter (M9–M10).

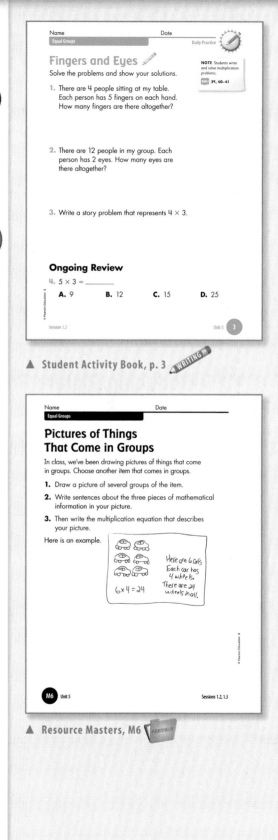

▲ **Student Activity Book, p. 3**

▲ **Resource Masters, M6**

Solving Multiplication Problems

Math Focus Points

◆ Using and understanding multiplication notation

◆ Writing and solving multiplication problems in context

Vocabulary
product

Today's Plan		Materials
ACTIVITY **1** Introducing *Counting Around the Class*	15 MIN CLASS	• Chart paper
ACTIVITY **2** Introducing Picture Problems	15 MIN CLASS PAIRS	• M6 (completed); T60
ACTIVITY **3** Solving Picture Problems	30 MIN PAIRS INDIVIDUALS	• *Student Activity Book,* pp. 4–6 • Connecting cubes
SESSION FOLLOW-UP **4** Daily Practice		• *Student Activity Book,* p. 7 • *Student Math Handbook,* pp. 39, 40–41

Ten-Minute Math

What Time Is It? What Time Will It Be? Show 8:45 on the demonstration clock.

What time is it on this clock?

If I start practicing my violin at 8:45 and I practice for 35 minutes, what time will it be when I finish practicing?

In pairs, students share ideas about what time they think it will be. As a class, make sure students can "cross over" the hour and focus on counting 35 by 5s. Ask students a similar question using 6:55 as the starting time and 45 minutes for duration.

Professional Development

❶ **Part 4: Ten-Minute Math and Classroom Routines** in *Implementing Investigations in Grade 3:* Counting Around the Class

ACTIVITY

① Introducing *Counting Around the Class*

15 MIN   CLASS

In this session, students are introduced to a new Ten-Minute Math activity. Students will continue to do this activity throughout this unit and the remainder of Grade 3. The activity helps students understand and practice multiplication.❶

Today we are going to learn a new activity called Counting Around the Class. In this activity we'll count by some number and each of you will take a turn. We are going to start today with a pattern you know, counting by 2s. The first person says "two," the next person says "four," the next says "six," and so on. But before we start counting, think about what number the last person will say. Try to figure it out without actually doing the counting. I'll take your predictions after you've thought for a minute.

Record student predictions on the board or chart paper. You may find that when students first learn this activity, some of their predictions may be unreasonable, particularly when counting by a number less familiar than two. To encourage students to think about number relationships when they make their predictions, choose a couple of close predictions and ask those students to explain their thinking.

[Bridget], you predicted that the last person to count will say the number [54]. What were you thinking about when you made your prediction? [Kenji], your prediction was [48]. How did you come up with that number?

Students might say:

"I know that 25 people counting would get us to 50 because 25 plus 25 is 50. But I think we have more than 25 people, so I guessed 54."

"I know that if you count by 2 ten times, that gets you to 20. Ten more times would get to 40. That would be 20 people. Our class has more than that, so I guessed 48."

"When you took attendance, we found out that there are 23 of us here today. If I double that, it's 46."

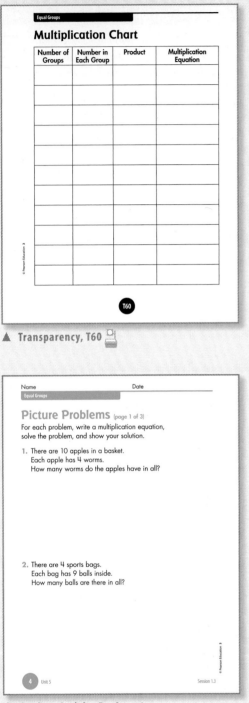

▲ Transparency, T60

▲ Student Activity Book, p. 4

Begin the count. Stop when a student says "20."

The last person to count just said "20." How many people have counted so far? See whether you can figure it out without counting each person.

Extend the activity by asking the following questions:

- If we continued counting around the class again, starting with the next number, what would the ending number be?

- Let's look at the predictions we made before we counted. Which of your predictions were possible? Think about the counting by 2s pattern. Are there any predictions that we couldn't have landed on?

15 MIN   CLASS   PAIRS

ACTIVITY

2 Introducing Picture Problems

Invite a few volunteers to share the multiplication pictures they made for homework (Pictures of Things That Come in Groups, M6). Then hold two of the pictures in your hand without showing them to the class. For each picture, ask a question in which the two factors are given and students must determine the product.

In this picture there are [4 flowers]. Each [flower] has [5 petals]. How many [petals] are there?

In this picture there are [3 girls]. Each [girl] has [8 braids]. How many [braids] are there?

Have students work in pairs to solve both problems. Elicit solutions from a couple of volunteers.

In the last math session, we talked about the three pieces of mathematical information in a multiplication situation. What information did I give you in each of the problems you just solved? What information was missing?

Students should understand that in both problems, the number of groups and the number in each group were given and the product was the missing information.

To make this clearer, display the transparency of the Multiplication Chart (T60) and work with students to fill in each column.

Number of Groups	Number in Each Group	Product	Multiplication Equation
4 flowers	5 petals	_____ petals in all	4 × 5 = _____
3 girls	8 braids	_____ braids in all	3 × 8 = _____

If you have not already done so, explain to students that the number of items in a multiplication situation is referred to as the *product.* Use this term for the rest of this unit. ❷

ACTIVITY

 ## 3 Solving Picture Problems

30 MIN · PAIRS · INDIVIDUALS

Working with a partner or on their own, students solve multiplication picture problems on *Student Activity Book* pages 4–6.

Note that there are two missing factor problems on these pages, one in which the number in each group is the missing information and one in which the number of groups is what needs to be determined. These missing factor problems are not the main focus of this session and will not be discussed in Session 4. However, most students should be able to solve these problems.

Also, do not expect students to use division notation at this time. Students will probably think of Problem 4, for example, as "five groups of what equal 30?" Help students use notation that will mirror that way of thinking about the problem, (5 × _____ = 30). Students will work more with missing factors in Investigation 2.

Name _____ **Date** _____
Equal Groups

Picture Problems (page 2 of 3)
For each problem, write a multiplication equation, solve the problem, and show your solution.

3. Alan sees 6 cars.
   Each car has 4 wheels.
   How many wheels does Alan see?

4. Mia has 5 packs of juice boxes.
   There are 30 juice boxes in all.
   The same number of juice boxes is in each pack.
   How many juice boxes are in each pack?

Session 1.3   Unit 5   **5**

▲ **Student Activity Book, p. 5**

ONGOING ASSESSMENT: Observing Students at Work

Students solve problems about multiplication illustrations.

- **What strategies are students using to solve these problems?**
  Are they drawing pictures and counting each object by 1s? Are they skip counting by the number in each group or using repeated addition? Are they using known multiplication combinations to help them find the product of a combination that they do not know?

- **Are students correctly using multiplication notation for each problem?**

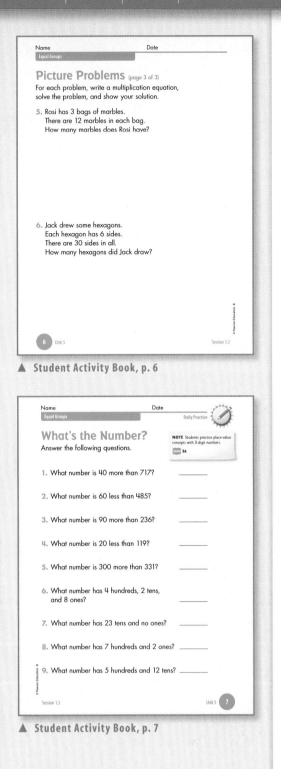

▲ **Student Activity Book, p. 6**

▲ **Student Activity Book, p. 7**

As you observe, look for examples of students using strategies that you would like to highlight in the discussion in Session 1.4.

DIFFERENTIATION: Supporting the Range of Learners

Intervention Students having difficulty visualizing these problems can benefit by representing each problem with cubes and responding to questions such as the following:

- How could you use these cubes to show the wheels on one car? How can that help you? Will it help to make another group of cubes to show the second car?

Ask questions such as the following to encourage students counting by 1s to count by groups or to use known multiplication combinations to solve each problem:

- Is there a faster way to count the number of wheels in your picture? Is there another number you can count by?

- The problem you are solving is about six cars with four wheels on each car. Do you know how many wheels two cars would have? What about three cars? Can you use 2×4 or 3×4 to help you solve this problem?

Continue helping students connect skip counting and repeated addition to multiplication by asking questions such as these:

- I see that you added 4s to find the answer. How many 4s did you add? How could you write this by using multiplication notation?

 SESSION FOLLOW-UP

Daily Practice

 Daily Practice: For ongoing review, have students complete *Student Activity Book* page 7.

Student Math Handbook: Students and families may use *Student Math Handbook* pages 39, 40–41 for reference and review. See pages 176–181 in the back of this unit.

Assessment: Solving Problems About Our Pictures

Math Focus Points

◆ Understanding the relationship among skip counting, repeated addition, and multiplication

◆ Writing and solving multiplication problems in context

◆ Using and understanding multiplication notation

Today's Plan		Materials
① DISCUSSION **Picture Problem Strategies**	🕐 20 MIN 👥 CLASS	
② ASSESSMENT ACTIVITY **Solving Problems About Our Pictures**	✓ 🕐 40 MIN 👤 INDIVIDUALS	• Class lists: "Things That Come in Groups"; unlined paper; colored pencils, markers, or crayons
③ SESSION FOLLOW-UP **Daily Practice and Homework**		• *Student Activity Book,* pp. 8–9 • *Student Math Handbook,* pp. 39, 40–41, 42

Ten-Minute Math

What Time Is It? Tell students the following story:

I walked to school today.

I left my house at 7:30 and arrived at school at 8:10. How long did it take me to get here?

In pairs, students share ideas about what they think. As a class, make sure students can visualize this new situation—finding the interval instead of finding the ending time. Collect answers and focus on strategies in which students count the interval by 5s, or other chunks (such as 30 minutes from 7:30–8:00 plus 10 minutes more to 8:10 makes 40 minutes total). Ask an additional similar question using 8:05 as the starting time and 8:55 as the end time.

Algebra Note

① Using the Associative Property Deondra's strategy is based on the associative property: $(9 \times 2) \times 2 = 9 \times (2 \times 2) = 9 \times 4$. At this grade level, students justify such arithmetic strategies by referring to the story contexts or describing mental images of the multiplicative situations they are representing. As students apply such strategies, ask them to explain the connections between the situation and the arithmetic. For more information, see Algebra Connections in This Unit on page 16.

DISCUSSION

① Picture Problem Strategies

20 MIN CLASS

Math Focus Points for Discussion

◆ Writing and solving multiplication problems in context

◆ Understanding the relationship among skip counting, repeated addition, and multiplication

Ask students you identified in Session 1.3 to share their strategies for solving problems with missing products. Ask questions to help students consider different ways to solve multiplication problems.

How many groups are in your problem? How many are in each group? What did you do first? Did you add each group together? Do you know how many are in two groups? How could that help you finish solving the problem?

Now ask for strategies for solving 4×9.

Students might say:

"I knew that $9 + 9 = 18$. Then I added another 9 to get to 27 and then another to get to 36."

"I added 9 plus 9 to get 18. Then I added two 18s to get to 36. So I know that there are 36 players on 4 teams. I wrote $9 + 9 = 18$ and $18 + 18 = 36$."

[Deondra] didn't know the product of 4×9, but she knew 2×9 and doubled it. How do we know that she has found the product for four groups of 9?

Help students think about how knowing two groups of 18 can help them solve 4×9. Continue to refer to examples in pictures as they explain their thinking.**①**

Differentiation

ASSESSMENT ACTIVITY

② Solving Problems About Our Pictures

40 MIN INDIVIDUALS

For this assessment, students return to the activity from Session 1.2 in which they chose items to illustrate from the class lists of "Things That Come in Groups." They write multiplication equations and sentences describing the number of groups, the number in each group, and the product. Students are assessed on the following benchmarks:

- Benchmark 1: Demonstrate an understanding of multiplication as involving groups of equal groups.

- Benchmark 3: Interpret and use multiplication notation.

Each of you will make another picture of groups from our lists of "Things That Come in Groups." Just like before, I want you to write three sentences about your picture that tell the number of groups you drew, the number in each group, and the product. On your paper, show how you found the product. Be sure to write a multiplication equation.②

As students are working, circulate to see if they are able to complete the task.

If students finish early, have them add more examples to the lists of "Things That Come in Groups," illustrate more multiplication situations, or solve one another's missing-product problems.

ONGOING ASSESSMENT: Observing Students at Work ✓

Students illustrate multiplication situations and solve problems about their pictures.

- **Are students able to recognize and write sentences about the mathematical information in the situations they illustrated?**

- **Are students finding the correct product for their illustrations?**

- **What strategies are students using to find the product in their multiplication situations?**

- **Are they counting by 1s, using repeated addition, skip counting groups, or using known multiplication combinations?**

Professional Development

❸ Teacher Note: Assessment: Solving Problems About Our Pictures, p. 149

Name	Date
Equal Groups	Daily Practice

Chapters, Slices, and Miles

Write multiplication equations, solve the problems, and show your solutions.

NOTE Students solve multiplication problems.
SMH 40–41

1. There are 3 books in a series. Each book has 11 chapters. If I read all of the books, how many chapters will I read altogether?

2. I have 4 pizzas. Each pizza has 8 slices. How many slices are there altogether?

3. George ran for 6 days. He ran 5 miles each day. How many miles did he run altogether?

Ongoing Review

4. Circle the equation that goes with the story below. Orange juice comes in packs of 4 cans. I have 5 packs of orange juice. How many cans of orange juice do I have?

A. $20 \times 4 = ?$ **C.** $9 \times 6 = ?$

B. $5 \times 4 = ?$ **D.** $5 \times 20 = ?$

8   Unit 5   Session 1.4

▲ **Student Activity Book, p. 8**

Name	Date
Equal Groups	Homework

More Picture Problems

For each problem, write a multiplication equation, solve the problem, and show your solution.

NOTE Students practice solving multiplication problems.
SMH 39, 40–41

1. In Kelley's picture there are 6 shirts. Each shirt has 6 buttons. How many buttons are there altogether?

2. Pilar brought 5 packs of crayons. There are 8 crayons in each pack. How many crayons are there altogether?

3. Benjamin drew a picture of some dogs. Each dog has 4 legs. There are 28 legs in the picture. How many dogs did he draw?

Session 1.4   Unit 5   9

▲ **Student Activity Book, p. 9**

DIFFERENTIATION: Supporting the Range of Learners

Extension This assessment activity gives students the opportunity to illustrate problems with larger numbers than they worked with in Session 1.2. For example, a student who illustrated a situation involving a group of three can work with a higher number in each group. Other students can illustrate and write problems about more than six groups. Help students choose appropriate numbers to work with.❸

Each student illustrates a multiplication situation; writes sentences that state the number of groups, the number in each group, and the product; and then writes a multiplication equation.

SESSION FOLLOW-UP

③ Daily Practice and Homework

 Daily Practice: For reinforcement of this unit's content, have students complete *Student Activity Book* page 8.

 Homework: On *Student Activity Book* page 9, students solve three multiplication problems and write an equation for each one.

 Student Math Handbook: Students and families may use *Student Math Handbook* pages 39, 40–41, 42 for reference and review. See pages 176–180 in the back of this unit.

Mathematical Emphases

Whole-Number Operations Understanding the meaning of multiplication

Math Focus Points

◆ Understanding the relationship among skip counting, repeated addition, and multiplication

◆ Writing and solving multiplication problems in context

Whole-Number Operations Reasoning about numbers and their factors and multiples

Math Focus Points

◆ Finding the multiples of the numbers 2, 3, 4, 5, 6, and 10 by skip counting

◆ Describing and comparing characteristics of the multiples of a number

◆ Understanding that doubling (or halving) one factor in a multiplication expression doubles (or halves) the product

Computation Fluency Learning the multiplication combinations with products up to 50 fluently

Math Focus Points

◆ Using known multiplication combinations to determine the product of more difficult combinations

Skip Counting and 100 Charts

	Student Activity Book	Student Math Handbook	Professional Development: Read Ahead of Time
SESSION 2.1 p. 48			
Highlighting Multiples on 100 Charts Students highlight the multiples of 2, 5, and 10. They look for relationships between the multiples of 5 and 10.	11–12	42, 43, 54–55	
SESSION 2.2 p. 53			
More Multiples Students discuss the relationships between the multiples of 5 and 10. They highlight the multiples of 3 and 6.	13	40–41, 42, 43	• **Teacher Note:** Patterns in the Skip Counting Charts, p. 152 • **Teacher Note:** Students' Problems with Skip Counting, p. 154 • **Dialogue Box:** Relationships Between the Multiples of 5 and 10, p. 170
SESSION 2.3 p. 59			
Solving Related Story Problems Students solve related story problems that encourage them to use the answer to one problem to help them solve another, larger problem.	14–18	44, 49–51	
SESSION 2.4 p. 64			
Patterns and Relationships Students look at the multiples of 3 and 6 together and discuss the patterns and relationships they see. They solve related problems involving groups of 3 and 6.	14–16, 19–21	42, 43	

Materials to Gather	Materials to Prepare
• **T61, 100 Chart with Skip Counting Circles** 🖨 • **Transparency pens in various colors** • **Colored pencils, markers, or crayons** • **Connecting cubes** (100 per pair)	• **M12, 100 Chart with Skip Counting Circles** Make copies. (3 per student, plus extras)
• **Students' "Multiples of 5" and "Multiples of 10" Charts** (from Session 2.1) • **Transparency pens in various colors** • **Colored pencils, markers, or crayons** • **Connecting cubes** (100 per pair, as needed)	• **M12, 100 Chart with Skip Counting Circles** Make copies. (2 per student, plus extras) • **T61, 100 Chart with Skip Counting Circles** 🖨 Make 4 copies, highlight all multiples of five on one copy and all multiples of 10 on another, and keep 2 copies blank.
• **Connecting cubes** (100 per pair, as needed)	• **M12, 100 Chart with Skip Counting Circles** Make copies. (1 per student)
• **Students' "Multiples of 3" and "Multiples of 6" Charts** (from Session 2.2) • **Colored pencils, markers, or crayons** • **Connecting cubes** (100 per pair, as needed)	• **M12, 100 Chart with Skip Counting Circles** Make copies. (as needed)

🖨 Overhead Transparency

Skip Counting and 100 Charts, *continued*

SESSION 2.5 p. 71	Student Activity Book	Student Math Handbook	Professional Development: Read Ahead of Time	
Assessment: Counting Around the Class Students share representations for the multiples of 3 and 6. They solve more multiplication problems and focus on using known combinations to solve more difficult problems. They are assessed on their ability to solve multiplication problems using skip counting or known combinations.	19–20, 22–24	39, 40–41, 42	• **Teacher Note:** Assessment: *Counting Around the Class,* p. 155 • **Dialogue Box:** Bags of 6, Bags of 3, p. 171	
SESSION 2.6 p. 76				
Using Multiplication Combinations Students solve more multiplication problems and focus on using known combinations to solve more difficult problems.	22, 25	40–41, 42, 43, 44		

Materials to Gather	Materials to Prepare
• Colored pencils, markers, or crayons	• M12, 100 Chart with Skip Counting Circles Make copies. (2 per student) • M13, Assessment: *Counting Around the Class* Make copies. (1 per student)

• M12, 100 Chart with Skip Counting Circles
  (2 per student; from Session 2.5)
• M13, Assessment: *Counting Around the Class*
  (1 per student; from Session 2.5)
• Colored pencils, markers, or crayons	

Highlighting Multiples on 100 Charts

Math Focus Points

◆ Finding the multiples of the numbers 2, 3, 4, 5, 6, and 10 by skip counting

◆ Describing and comparing characteristics of the multiples of a number

◆ Understanding the relationship among skip counting, repeated addition, and multiplication

Vocabulary

multiple

Today's Plan		Materials
ACTIVITY **1** **Highlighting the Multiples of 2**	25 MIN CLASS INDIVIDUALS	• M12*; T61 • Transparency pens in various colors; colored pencils, markers, or crayons
ACTIVITY **2** **Multiples of 5 and 10**	35 MIN PAIRS INDIVIDUALS	• M12* • Connecting cubes; colored pencils, markers, or crayons
SESSION FOLLOW-UP **3** **Daily Practice and Homework**		• *Student Activity Book*, pp. 11–12 • *Student Math Handbook*, pp. 42, 43, 54–55

*See *Materials to Prepare*, p. 45.

Ten-Minute Math

Counting Around the Class Students count around the class by 5s. Each student says another multiple of 5 until all students have counted once. Highlight the multiples of 5 by writing them on the board as students say them. Ask how many students have counted at 30, 60, and 90.

25 MIN   CLASS   INDIVIDUALS

ACTIVITY

1 Highlighting the Multiples of 2

Display the transparency of 100 Chart with Skip Counting Circles (T61) and label it "Multiples of 2."

For the next few days we will be counting by different groups and using these 100 charts to record our work. Now I want to highlight the numbers that we say when we skip count by 2. These numbers are the multiples of 2. What are the first few numbers we will land on if we count by 2s?

Highlight numbers on the 100 chart according to your students' instructions. The highlighting can be done in any way that shows the patterns clearly but leaves the numbers easy to read: circling, underlining, shading in lightly, or outlining the frames around the numbers. After enough numbers have been highlighted to begin to form a pattern, ask students to name multiples of 2 among the numbers over 50 (skipping around, not in order). After highlighting about half the multiples of 2, ask students to name any patterns they see that will help in filling out the rest of the chart.❶

Multiples of 2

1	2	3	4	5	6	7	8	9	10
11	12	13	14	15	16	17	18	19	20
21	22	23	24	25	26	27	28	29	30
31	32	33	34	35	36	37	38	39	40
41	42	43	44	45	46	47	48	49	50
51	52	53	54	55	56	57	58	59	60
61	62	63	64	65	66	67	68	69	70
71	72	73	74	75	76	77	78	79	80
81	82	83	84	85	86	87	88	89	90
91	92	93	94	95	96	97	98	99	100

Math Note

❶ **Row vs. Column** Students often confuse the words *row* and *column*, describing a pattern as going "down the row" rather than "down the column." When students do not use these words in the conventional way, ask them to explain or demonstrate what they mean so that the focus is on their good mathematical thinking, not on getting the words right. Keep using the terms yourself so that students continually hear them used correctly in context. Other terms that may come up in this context that may need some explanation are *horizontal*, *vertical*, and *diagonal*.

Name _____ Date _____

Equal Groups

100 Chart with Skip Counting Circles

1	2	3	4	5	6	7	8	9	10
11	12	13	14	15	16	17	18	19	20
21	22	23	24	25	26	27	28	29	30
31	32	33	34	35	36	37	38	39	40
41	42	43	44	45	46	47	48	49	50
51	52	53	54	55	56	57	58	59	60
61	62	63	64	65	66	67	68	69	70
71	72	73	74	75	76	77	78	79	80
81	82	83	84	85	86	87	88	89	90
91	92	93	94	95	96	97	98	99	100

1× __ 2× __ 3× __ 4× __ 5× __ 6× __ 7× __ 8× __ 9× __ 10× __

11× __ 12× __ 13× __ 14× __ 15× __ 16× __ 17× __ 18× __ 19× __ 20× __

21× __ 22× __ 23× __ 24× __ 25× __ 26× __ 27× __ 28× __ 29× __ 30× __

M12 Unit 5   Sessions 2.1, 2.2, 2.3, 2.4, 2.5, 2.6

▲ **Resource Masters, M12; T61**

❷ **Creating a Book of Highlighted 100 Charts** In this investigation, students highlight the multiples of the numbers 2–6 and 10 on copies of the 100 Chart with Skip Counting Circles (M12). (Some students may complete charts for other numbers as well.) At the end of the investigation, you may want to staple these sheets together so that students have them available as a reference for solving problems that involve groups.

Students should notice the patterns of highlighted numbers in the columns under 2, 4, 6, 8, and 10 and the fact that the multiples of 2 are all even numbers.

Next, students fill in their own 100 Chart with Skip Counting Circles (M12). Have students label the top of the chart "Multiples of 2" and highlight those numbers. Suggest that they begin by marking lightly with pencil so that they can erase any mistakes. After completing about three rows, students check with a partner to make sure that they are on the right track before completing the chart with a permanent color.

When students are finished, direct their attention to the skip counting circles on the bottom of 100 Chart with Skip Counting Circles (M12). These circles are designed for two purposes: to help students make the connection between skip counting and multiplication and to help them become familiar with multiplication combinations. Explain to students that they should write the numeral 2 in each of the blanks and fill in the circles with the corresponding multiples, as shown below.❷

$1 \times \underline{2}$	$2 \times \underline{2}$	$3 \times \underline{2}$	$4 \times \underline{2}$	$5 \times \underline{\ }$	$6 \times \underline{\ }$	$7 \times \underline{\ }$	$8 \times \underline{\ }$	$9 \times \underline{\ }$	$10 \times \underline{\ }$
(2)	(4)	(6)	(8)	( )	( )	( )	( )	( )	( )

$11 \times \underline{2}$	$12 \times \underline{2}$	$13 \times \underline{2}$	$14 \times \underline{2}$	$15 \times \underline{\ }$	$16 \times \underline{\ }$	$17 \times \underline{\ }$	$18 \times \underline{\ }$	$19 \times \underline{\ }$	$20 \times \underline{\ }$
( )	( )	( )	( )	( )	( )	( )	( )	( )	( )

$21 \times \underline{2}$	$22 \times \underline{2}$	$23 \times \underline{2}$	$24 \times \underline{2}$	$25 \times \underline{\ }$	$26 \times \underline{\ }$	$27 \times \underline{\ }$	$28 \times \underline{\ }$	$29 \times \underline{\ }$	$30 \times \underline{\ }$
( )	( )	( )	( )	( )	( )	( )	( )	( )	( )

ONGOING ASSESSMENT: Observing Students at Work

Students skip count to highlight the multiples of 2 on a 100 chart.

- **Can students skip count accurately by 2?**

- **Can students identify the multiples of 2?**

ACTIVITY

35 MIN   PAIRS   INDIVIDUALS

Multiples of 5 and 10

For the first 15 minutes, students work in pairs to make towers of connecting cubes. First have partners use all of their 100 connecting cubes to make towers of 10.

How many towers of ten cubes do you need to make a total of 100?

Now have students go on to think about towers of five.

How many towers of five will you need to make a total of 100 cubes? Is there some way you can use your towers of ten to help you figure this out?

Give students a few minutes to work on finding towers of five.

How many towers of five do you think it will take to make 100? Do you think there will be more towers of five than of ten? What is the relationship between five and ten?

Next, distribute two more copies of the 100 Chart with Skip Counting Circles (M12) to each student.

A student makes her own skip counting sheets for 5 and 10 and fills in the circles at the bottom of the page.

As students are finishing, encourage them to share their ideas about the relationship between the multiples of 5 and 10. Ask them to think about the towers they built as well as the charts they filled out. Also explain that they will be thinking more about the relationship between 5 and 10 and other doubles in the next few sessions.

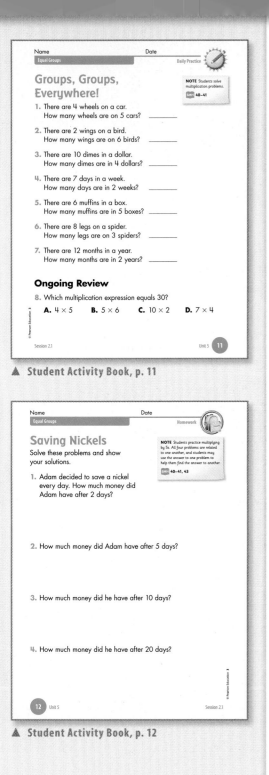

▲ Student Activity Book, p. 11

▲ Student Activity Book, p. 12

ONGOING ASSESSMENT: Observing Students at Work

Students explore the multiples of 5 and 10 and look for patterns in these multiples.

- ### Can students accurately count by 5s and 10s?

As students work to fill out their charts, ask them what they notice about the relationship between the multiples of 5 and 10. Some students may notice that the multiples of 5 are half as big as the corresponding multiples of 10.

DIFFERENTIATION: Supporting the Range of Learners

Intervention When filling in the skip counting circles, some students will need support in finding the multiples of 5 and 10 that are beyond those highlighted on their 100 charts. Encourage those students to look for patterns in the skip counting circles—such as the 5, 0, 5, 0 in the ones place for the multiples of 5 and the 0s in the ones place for the multiples of 10—that will help them determine these multiples. In addition, help students consider how knowing that $10 \times 5 = 50$ and $20 \times 5 = 100$ can help them figure out 30×5.

SESSION FOLLOW-UP

③ Daily Practice and Homework

 Daily Practice: For reinforcement of this unit's content, have students complete *Student Activity Book* page 11.

 Homework: On *Student Activity Book* page 12, students figure out how much money Adam has saved after 2, 5, 10, and 20 days.

Student Math Handbook: Students and families may use *Student Math Handbook* pages 42, 43, 54–55 for reference and review. See pages 176–181 in the back of this unit.

More Multiples

Math Focus Points

◆ Finding the multiples of the numbers 2, 3, 4, 5, 6, and 10 by skip counting

◆ Describing and comparing characteristics of the multiples of a number

◆ Understanding that doubling (or halving) one factor in a multiplication expression doubles (or halves) the product

Today's Plan		Materials
DISCUSSION ① **Relationships Between the Multiples of 5 and 10**	🕐 25 MIN 👥 CLASS 👥 PAIRS	• T61 📇 * • Students' "Multiples of 5" and "Multiples of 10" Charts (from Session 2.1)
ACTIVITY ② **Highlighting the Multiples of 3 and 6**	🕐 35 MIN 👥 CLASS 👥 PAIRS	• T61 📇; M12* • Transparency pens in various colors; colored pencils, markers, or crayons; connecting cubes (100 per pair, as needed)
SESSION FOLLOW-UP ③ **Daily Practice**		• *Student Activity Book*, p. 13 • *Student Math Handbook*, pp. 40–41, 42, 43

*See *Materials to Prepare*, p. 45.

Ten-Minute Math

Counting Around the Class Students count around the class by 10s. Ask for predictions for what the last number will be.

Will it be larger or smaller than when we counted by 5s? How much larger or smaller?

Each student says another multiple of 10 until all students have counted once.

Highlight the multiples of 10 by writing them on the board as students say them. Ask how many students have counted at 80, 160, and 200.

① Relationships Between the Multiples of 5 and 10

25 MIN CLASS PAIRS

Math Focus Points for Discussion

◆ Describing and comparing characteristics of the multiples of a number

In our last math class, you found the multiples of 5 and 10. Let's look at the patterns we see in these two charts. What do you notice about the multiples of 5 and 10? Look at your 100 chart as well as the circles of multiples you filled in underneath.

List the patterns on the board or on chart paper.

> The multiples of 10 all end in 0.
>
> The multiples of 5 end in 0 or 5.
>
> The multiples of 10 are all even numbers.
>
> The multiples of 5 are in a sequence of odd, even, odd, even, and so on.

Place the transparencies of "Multiples of 5" and "Multiples of 10" prepared from 100 Chart with Skip Counting Circles (T61) on top of each other on the overhead.

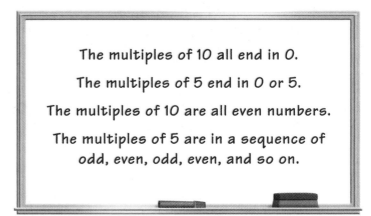

Now we'll think about how these multiples are related to each other. What do you notice when you look at the multiples of 5 and 10 together? Place your charts next to each other in front of you as you think about this.❶

Students might say:

 "When I look at the circles of multiples, I see that every other multiple of 5 is a multiple of 10."

 "All the multiples of 5 and 10 end in either 5 or 0."

 "The 10s multiples go up faster than the 5s. If I jump three times on the 10s chart I get to 30. If I jump three times on the 5s chart, I only get to 15."

 "There are twice as many multiples of 5 on the 100 chart as there are multiples of 10."

I heard [Zhang] say that three 10s get you to 30 but three 5s only get you to 15. [Write $3 \times 10 = 30$ and $3 \times 5 = 15$ on the board.] You get twice as far when you count by 10 as when you count by 5. I wonder whether that same relationship is true if you count by 3 and 6 or by 4 and 8? What do you land on when you count three 4s? What about three 8s?❷

Write $3 \times 4 =$ and $3 \times 8 =$ on the board. Collect the answers to these equations and point out that you have taken three jumps of each number but the number you land on is twice as much when you count by 8.

I heard several of you say something about eight is twice four so the answer is twice as much. This sounds very interesting! Do you think this is true for higher numbers? If I count by 12 and 24, will each multiple of 24 be twice as much as the same multiple of 12? We will be talking more about this over the next few days.

Professional Development

❶ **Dialogue Box:** Relationships Between the Multiples of 5 and 10, p. 170

Math Note

❷ **Relationships Between Multiples** Students will continue to look at relationships between multiples of related numbers throughout this unit and will consider what happens to the product of a multiplication expression when one factor is doubled or halved. For example, if a student knows that $3 \times 4 = 12$, how can that combination be used to find the product of 3×8? Understanding these relationships and why they work will help students learn their multiplication combinations and develop strategies for solving more complex problems in the future (e.g., $68 \times 5 = (68 \times 10) \div 2$). Keep in mind that these ideas take time to develop and not all students will grasp them at the same time.

Professional Development

❸ Teacher Note: Patterns in the Skip Counting Charts, p. 152

Math Note

❹ Even and Odd These words will come up in students' descriptions of patterns on the 100 charts. Students investigated the meaning of odd and even numbers in Grade 2. However, students have more to learn about odd and even numbers in this context. For example, some students believe at first that because multiples of even numbers, such as 2 or 10, are all even, that multiples of odd numbers should all be odd. Be sure to ask students what they mean by *even* and *odd*. How do they know that a number is even or odd? Why are all the multiples of 5 not odd? Students can refer to *Even Numbers* and *Odd Numbers* in the *Student Math Handbook* for more about the meanings of *odd* and *even*.

35 MIN   CLASS   PAIRS

ACTIVITY

② Highlighting the Multiples of 3 and 6

Project a clean transparency of the 100 Chart with Skip Counting Circles (T61) and label it "Multiples of 3."

In our last math class, we highlighted the multiples of 2, 5, and 10 on our 100 charts. This chart will be about numbers that make groups of 3, so I'm labeling it "Multiples of 3."

Highlight the multiples of 3, following your students' instructions. Again, encourage students to skip around on the chart and to name some multiples of 3 higher than 50.

What patterns do you see? What's different about the patterns the 3s make and the patterns you observed in the multiples of 2, 5, and 10? ❸

Multiples of 3

1	2	3	4	5	6	7	8	9	10
11	12	13	14	15	16	17	18	19	20
21	22	23	24	25	26	27	28	29	30
31	32	33	34	35	36	37	38	39	40
41	42	43	44	45	46	47	48	49	50
51	52	53	54	55	56	57	58	59	60
61	62	63	64	65	66	67	68	69	70
71	72	73	74	75	76	77	78	79	80
81	82	83	84	85	86	87	88	89	90
91	92	93	94	95	96	97	98	99	100

Students might say:

"The multiples of 2, 5, and 10 make columns while the multiples of 3 make a diagonal pattern."

"The multiples of 2 and 10 are all even numbers while the multiples of 3 are odd, even, odd, even, like the multiples of 5." ❹

Some students may notice that, unlike the multiples of 2, 5 and 10, multiples of 3 can have any digit in the ones place. Consequently, looking at that digit is not helpful for recognizing multiples of 3. Other students may notice that there is a repeating pattern in the ones digit when they see the 3, 6, 9 sequence occur again at 33, 36, 39.

Distribute two copies of the 100 Chart with Skip Counting Circles (M12) to each student. Have students label one "Multiples of 3" and the other "Multiples of 6." Tell students to highlight these multiples, reminding them to think about how they can use the patterns they observed to help them.

When the multiples are highlighted, students fill in the skip counting circles at the bottom of the page. Because highlighting the multiples of 6 will not be done as a full-class activity, it is important that each student works with a partner so they can double-check each other's work. Be aware that for the multiples of 6, the skip counting circles continue past those multiples that students will have highlighted on their 100 charts.

ONGOING ASSESSMENT: Observing Students at Work

Students highlight the multiples of 3 and 6 and relate these multiples to multiplication combinations by filling in the skip counting circles.

- **Are students using the patterns they have identified on their 100 charts to check their work?**

- **Are students able to fill in the skip counting circles for the multiples of 6 beyond those highlighted on their 100 charts?**

DIFFERENTIATION: Supporting the Range of Learners

(Intervention) Some problems may arise for students when doing this activity. Help students who are having difficulty in the following ways.⑤

- **Suggest that the students count quietly between multiples.** For example, when highlighting the multiples of 3, students would say 1, 2, 3, 4, 5, 6, 7, 8, 9, 10, 11, 12, 13, 14, 15, and so on.

- **If you see a student who has miscounted on the 100 chart, call the student's attention to patterns on the chart with questions such as the following:**

  - Is there a pattern that you notice on your 3s (or 6s) chart? Is this pattern continuing all the way to the bottom of the chart?

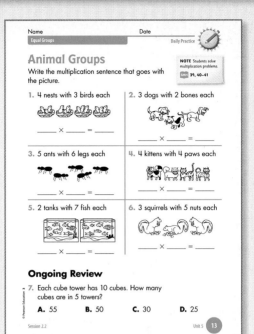

▲ Student Activity Book, p. 13

● **Have students double-check one another's charts.** When two or three students compare charts, they can often find and correct their own miscounting.

● **Some students may be having trouble understanding what they are doing when they "count by" a number on their 100 charts.** Suggest that these students use cubes to help them visualize what is happening each time they count to the next multiple. For example, when counting by 3s, students make a group of 3 cubes and then mark 3 on their 100 charts, make another group of 3 and mark 6 on their charts, and so on. Students will naturally stop using the cubes when they are ready.

When filling in the skip counting circles, some students will need support in finding the multiples of 6 that are beyond those highlighted on their 100 charts (102, 108, 114, 120). Encourage those students to look for patterns in the skip counting circles, such as the 6, 2, 8, 4, 0, pattern in the ones digits, that will help them determine these multiples. In addition, help students consider how knowing that $10 \times 6 = 60$ can help them figure out that $20 \times 6 = 120$.

SESSION FOLLOW-UP

 Daily Practice

 Daily Practice: For reinforcement of this unit's content, have students complete *Student Activity Book* page 13.

Student Math Handbook: Students and families may use *Student Math Handbook* pages 40–41, 42, 43 for reference and review. See pages 176–181 in the back of this unit.

Solving Related Story Problems

Math Focus Points

◆ Using known multiplication combinations to determine the product of more difficult combinations

◆ Understanding that doubling (or halving) one factor in a multiplication expression doubles (or halves) the product

◆ Writing and solving multiplication problems in context

Today's Plan		Materials
① DISCUSSION **Introducing Related Problems**	20 MIN · CLASS · PAIRS	
② ACTIVITY **Solving Related Problems**	40 MIN · PAIRS · INDIVIDUALS	• *Student Activity Book*, pp. 14–16 • M12* • Connecting cubes (100 per pair, as needed)
③ SESSION FOLLOW-UP **Daily Practice and Homework**		• *Student Activity Book*, pp. 17–18 • *Student Math Handbook*, pp. 44, 49–51

*See *Materials to Prepare*, p. 45.

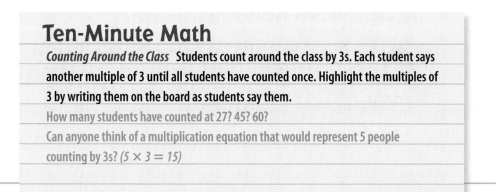

Ten-Minute Math

Counting Around the Class Students count around the class by 3s. Each student says another multiple of 3 until all students have counted once. Highlight the multiples of 3 by writing them on the board as students say them.

How many students have counted at 27? 45? 60?

Can anyone think of a multiplication equation that would represent 5 people counting by 3s? *(5 × 3 = 15)*

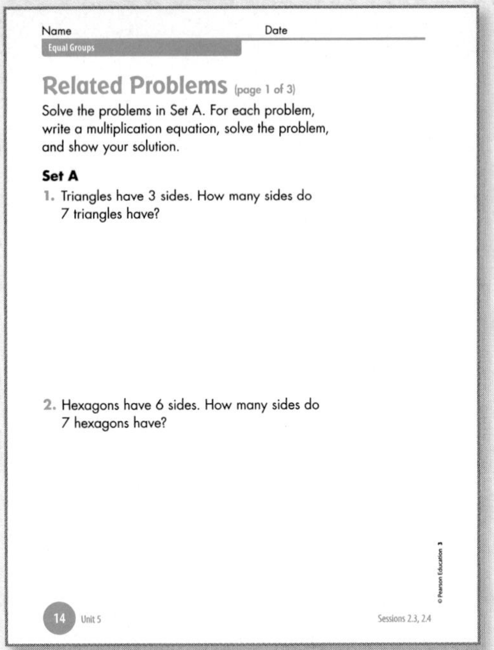
Name Date

Equal Groups

Related Problems (page 1 of 3)

Solve the problems in Set A. For each problem, write a multiplication equation, solve the problem, and show your solution.

Set A

1. Triangles have 3 sides. How many sides do 7 triangles have?

2. Hexagons have 6 sides. How many sides do 7 hexagons have?

© Pearson Education 3

14 Unit 5 Sessions 2.3, 2.4

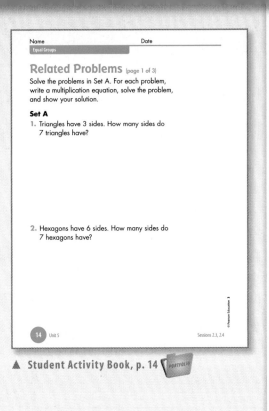

▲ Student Activity Book, p. 14 PORTFOLIO

DISCUSSION

1 Introducing Related Problems

20 MIN CLASS PAIRS

Math Focus Points for Discussion

- Understanding that doubling (or halving) one factor in a multiplication expression doubles (or halves) the product

Write the following two problems on the board:

> Mrs. Johnson's class counted around the class by 3s. What number did the fourth person say?
>
> Later, the class counted around by 6s. What number did the fourth person say?

Work with a partner to solve these problems. Write a multiplication equation for each problem. Then talk about how they are related. What is the same about these problems and what is different?

Bring the class together and ask students for the multiplication equations for each problem. ($4 \times 3 = 12$; $4 \times 6 = 24$)

I noticed that when our class counted by 6s, the fourth person said a larger number than when they counted by 3s. Why do you think that is? What else do you notice? Can you explain your ideas, using a picture or a skip counting chart?

Students might say:

"Look at my 100 chart. Each jump of 6 is bigger than each jump of 3, so if you make jumps of 6, you will get to a higher number."

"I can show it with the circles on the bottom of the chart. In the fourth circle, I am at 12 when I count by 3, and I am at 24 when I count by 6. 24 is a lot more than 12!"

"If you have four bunches of flowers, and each bunch has 3, you just have 3, 3, 3, 3. But if each bunch has 6, you have 6, 6, 6, 6."

Here is one more example. This time, when Mrs. Johnson's class counted by 3s, she stopped at the fifth person. What number did the fifth person say?

Try it with the class and record the following:

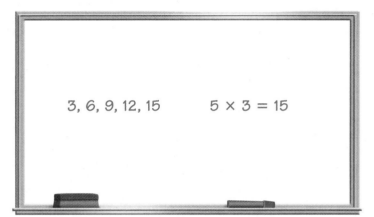

3, 6, 9, 12, 15   5 × 3 = 15

What if they counted by 6s? What number do you think the fifth person would say now? Why do you think so?

Collect a few brief responses. Students may be able to recognize that, because 6 is twice as large as 3, the product will be twice as large. Students will return to this idea in Session 2.4.

ACTIVITY

40 MIN   PAIRS   INDIVIDUALS

2 Solving Related Problems

Students work with partners or on their own to solve the problems on *Student Activity Book* pages 14–16. All of the problems encourage students to use the answer to the first problem to solve the second problem. For example, if you know how many yogurts there are in three packages, how can that help you figure out how many yogurts are in six packages?

As students work, ask them whether some of the problems helped them solve any of the other problems. Encourage students to begin to use combinations they know to solve each of these problems. When students have finished working on these pages, have them make a chart of the multiples of 4 on M12. They go on to complete any unfinished work on their 2, 3, 5, and 10 skip counting charts.

Name _____ Date _____
Equal Groups

Related Problems (page 2 of 3)

Solve the problems in Set B. For each problem, complete the multiplication equation, solve the problem, and show your solution.

Set B

1. Nancy and Philip were finding multiples on their skip counting charts. They circled 42 on the 6s chart. How many jumps of 6 did they take to get to 42?

   _____ × 6 = 42

2. Deondra and Kenji circled 42 on the 3s chart. How many jumps of 3 did they take to get to 42? Show how you got your answer.

   _____ × 3 = 42

Sessions 2.3, 2.4   Unit 5   15

▲ **Student Activity Book, p. 15**

Name _____ Date _____
Equal Groups

Related Problems (page 3 of 3)

Solve the problems in Set C and Set D. For each problem, write a multiplication equation, solve the problem, and show your solution.

Set C

1. Oscar bought juice boxes that come in packages of 6. He bought 5 packs. How many juice boxes did he buy?

2. Pilar bought 8 packs of juice boxes. How many juice boxes did she buy?

Set D

1. Deondra noticed 7 children outside her house, each riding a tricycle. How many wheels were there altogether?

2. Two more children rode up on tricycles. How many wheels were there then?

Choose one set (A, B, C, or D) and explain how the first problem could help you solve the second problem. Write your answer on another sheet of paper.

16   Unit 5   Sessions 2.3, 2.4

▲ **Student Activity Book, p. 16** WRITING

ONGOING ASSESSMENT: Observing Students at Work

Students solve sets of related multiplication problems in which the factors are related to one another.

- **Can students solve story problems that involve multiplication?**

- **Do students notice the double and half relationship between the numbers within Set A and Set B?**

- **Are students using one problem to help them solve the other?**

As students work, ask questions to help them see how to use one answer to find another.

- I see you figured out how many sides are in seven triangles. Can you predict how many sides are in seven hexagons? What is the relationship between 3 and 6 (4 and 8, etc.)? How do the numbers change in each equation? Why do you think that is? Does your answer to the first problem help you find the answer to the second problem?

DIFFERENTIATION: Supporting the Range of Learners

Intervention Suggest to students who are having trouble seeing the relationship between groups of 3 and 6, or of 5 and 10, to use cubes to model each problem.

Number lines can also be a useful representation of the relationship between groups.

3 Daily Practice and Homework

Daily Practice: For reinforcement of this unit's content, have students complete *Student Activity Book* page 17.

Homework: Students solve three pairs of related multiplication problems on *Student Activity Book* page 18, explaining how they used the first problem in the pair to help them solve the second problem in the pair.

Student Math Handbook: Students and families may use *Student Math Handbook* pages 44, 49–51 for reference and review. See pages 176–181 in the back of this unit.

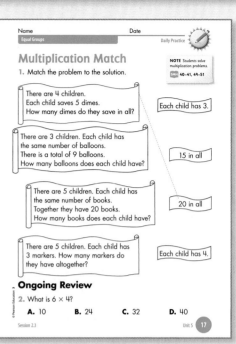

▲ Student Activity Book, p. 17

▲ Student Activity Book, p. 18

Patterns and Relationships

Math Focus Points

◆ Describing and comparing characteristics of the multiples of a number

◆ Using known multiplication combinations to determine the product of more difficult combinations

◆ Understanding that doubling (or halving) one factor in a multiplication expression doubles (or halves) the product

Today's Plan		Materials
① DISCUSSION **Strategies for Solving Related Problems**	🕐 20 MIN 👥 CLASS	• *Student Activity Book*, pp. 14–16 (completed)
② ACTIVITY **Representing the Multiples of 3 and 6**	🕐 40 MIN 👥 CLASS 👥 PAIRS	• *Student Activity Book*, pp. 19–20 • M12* • Students' "Multiples of 3" and "Multiples of 6" Charts (from Session 2.2); colored pencils, markers, or crayons; connecting cubes (100 per pair, as needed)
③ SESSION FOLLOW-UP **Daily Practice**		• *Student Activity Book*, p. 21 • *Student Math Handbook*, pp. 42, 43

*See *Materials to Prepare*, p. 45.

Ten-Minute Math

Counting Around the Class Students count around the class by 6s. Each student says another multiple of 6 until all students have counted once. Highlight the multiples of 6 by writing them on the board as students say them.

How many students have counted at 36? 60? 150?

Can anyone think of a multiplication equation that would represent 5 people counting by 6s? ($5 \times 6 = 30$).

DISCUSSION

1 Strategies for Solving Related Problems

Math Focus Points for Discussion

◆ Using known multiplication combinations to determine the product of more difficult combinations

Choose any one of the related problem sets from *Student Activity Book* pages 14–16 to discuss as a class. Write the problems you chose on the board. The problems in Set C are shown below.

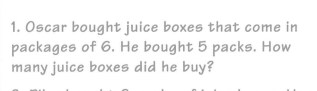

1. Oscar bought juice boxes that come in packages of 6. He bought 5 packs. How many juice boxes did he buy?

2. Pilar bought 8 packs of juice boxes. How many juice boxes did she buy?

Let's look at one of the Related Problem sets you worked on yesterday. How did you figure out each answer? Explain what you did, including any tools you used. Think about ways that you could have used the answer to the first problem to help you figure out the answer to the second problem.

Students might say:

"I drew five circles and put six dots inside each one. I counted by 6s to get to 30. Then I added three more circles on to my picture (so that I had eight circles total) and kept counting by 6s until I got to 48."

"I looked at the circles on the bottom of my Multiples of 6 sheet. I counted five groups to 30, and then three more groups to 48. So I counted eight groups in all."

"I knew that 5 x 6 is 30. I knew that I needed three more groups of 6 to get to 8 groups. And 3 × 6 = 18. So I added 30 + 18 = 48."

So when you solved five groups of juice boxes, you really found part of the answer to eight groups of juice boxes. How did you know that you needed three more groups—that is, why did you decide to multiply 3 × 6 next?

Collect students' responses and highlight the idea that one way to solve a multiplication problem is to break the total number of groups into smaller groups of groups, find the products of the smaller groups, and then add all the products together.

ACTIVITY

40 MIN   **CLASS**   **PAIRS**

2 Representing the Multiples of 3 and 6

Make sure that students have their "Multiples of 3" and "Multiples of 6" charts in front of them, as well as connecting cubes as needed.

Do you remember when we were talking about counting by 6s and counting by 3s? Some of you had some ideas about doubling. We're going to talk about those ideas again, but first let's count by 6s and by 3s.

Ask students to count with you by 6s up to 60. Students can use their charts of multiples of 3 and 6 to help them count. If some students are thinking through how to count by 6s or 3s, you may want to stop at some numbers and ask students to explain how they would figure out what number is next without looking at their charts.

Record the sequence of the first ten multiples of 6 on the board. Then count by 3s and record the first ten multiples of 3 right under the multiples of 6. Your board will look like the following:

6	12	18	24	30	36	42	48	54	60
3	6	9	12	15	18	21	24	27	30

Ask students what they notice about the two lists of multiples.

Students might say:

 "I notice that 15 in the 3s list is half of 30 in the 6s list, which is right above it. If you count around the class by 6s, the fifth person says 30; if you count around by 3s, the fifth person says 15."

Is this true for other pairs of numbers? What does the eighth person say if you count by 6s? By 3s? What about the tenth person? What if we kept going? Would the next multiple of 6 be double the next multiple of 3? Why is this happening? Who has some ideas?

After a few ideas have been expressed, pose the following story problem about packaging something in groups of 3 and then in groups of 6.

Ms. Ross owns an apple orchard. She was making bags to sell with three apples in each bag. If she made ten bags of apples, how many apples did she use? On another day, she decided to put six apples in each bag. If she made ten bags of apples, how many apples did she use this time?

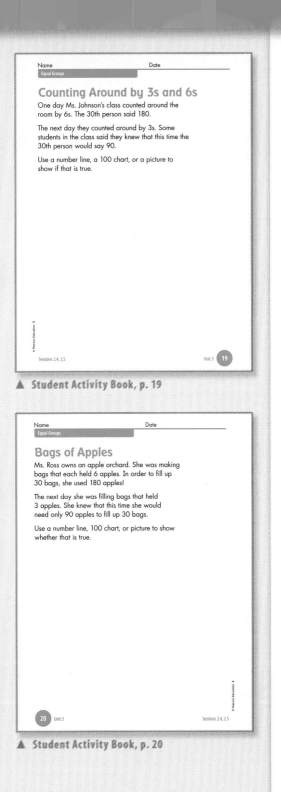

Name _____ Date _____

Equal Groups

Counting Around by 3s and 6s

One day Ms. Johnson's class counted around the room by 6s. The 30th person said 180.

The next day they counted around by 3s. Some students in the class said they knew that this time the 30th person would say 90.

Use a number line, a 100 chart, or a picture to show if that is true.

Sessions 2.4, 2.5   Unit 5   **19**

▲ **Student Activity Book, p. 19**

Name _____ Date _____

Equal Groups

Bags of Apples

Ms. Ross owns an apple orchard. She was making bags that each held 6 apples. In order to fill up 30 bags, she used 180 apples!

The next day she was filling bags that held 3 apples. She knew that this time she would need only 90 apples to fill up 30 bags.

Use a number line, 100 chart, or picture to show whether that is true.

20   Unit 5   Sessions 2.4, 2.5

▲ **Student Activity Book, p. 20**

Students can work on the problems for a few minutes in pairs. Ask students for their solutions and write them on the board, using words and equations.

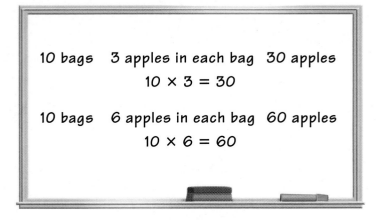

$$10 \text{ bags} \quad 3 \text{ apples in each bag} \quad 30 \text{ apples}$$
$$10 \times 3 = 30$$

$$10 \text{ bags} \quad 6 \text{ apples in each bag} \quad 60 \text{ apples}$$
$$10 \times 6 = 60$$

Some of you noticed that there are twice as many apples when she puts six apples in each bag. Why is that? Does this remind anyone of what happened when we counted by 6s and 3s?

Now introduce the next task.

I'd like you to choose one of these situations—either counting around by 3s and 6s or filling bags with three apples and then with six apples. If you choose counting around by 3s and 6s, think about which number the twentieth person says in both cases. Think about the number the thirtieth person says. Try some other numbers. If you choose bags of apples, think about how many apples are in 20 bags if you put three in a bag and if you put six in a bag. Think about 30 bags. Try some other numbers. Whichever situation you choose, use a drawing to show your ideas. If you want to use cubes, then make a drawing to show what you did with them.

Students choose to work on either *Student Activity Book* page 19 or page 20. Distribute copies of the 100 Chart with Skip Counting Circles (M12) for students to use as needed.

ONGOING ASSESSMENT: Observing Students at Work

A student creates a representation to show that the thirtieth multiple of 3 is half of the thirtieth multiple of 6.

Look for a range of examples of representations that show the relationship between groups of 6 and groups of 3 to share in the next session.

- **Can students show that the thirtieth multiple of 3 is 90?**

- **Can they create a representation that shows that the thirtieth multiple of 3 is half as much as the thirtieth multiple of 6?**

As students work, ask them questions such as the following:

Where are the groups of 6? The groups of 3? How did Ms. Ross know she would need 90 apples? How does your representation show that?

DIFFERENTIATION: Supporting the Range of Learners

(Intervention) Encourage students who are unclear how to begin to first show whether the thirtieth person counting by 3s says 90 or whether 30 bags of 3 apples contain 90 apples. They can then show, using the same kind of representation, how they know that the thirtieth person says 180 when counting by 6s or that 30 bags of 6 apples contain 180 apples. Then compare the two representations. What do students notice? Can students see groups of three anywhere in their representations of 6s or vice versa? It may help some students to work with smaller numbers. They may solve the same problems but work on ten bags of apples (or the tenth person).

Student Activity Book page:

Name _____ Date _____
Equal Groups   Daily Practice

Adding 10s and 100s

Solve the following sets of related problems.
Think about how to use one problem to solve
the next one.

NOTE Students practice
solving addition problems
in related sets.
SMH 20–24, 36

1. 175 + 20 = _____	2. 235 + 100 = _____
175 + 30 = _____	235 + 200 = _____
175 + 40 = _____	235 + 300 = _____
3. 72 + 30 = _____	4. 264 + 30 = _____
72 + 130 = _____	264 + 40 = _____
72 + 230 = _____	264 + 50 = _____
5. 308 + 40 = _____	6. 144 + 130 = _____
328 + 40 = _____	144 + 140 = _____
348 + 40 = _____	144 + 150 = _____

© Pearson Education 3

Session 2.4   Unit 5   **21**

▲ Student Activity Book, p. 21

Extension Ask students who finish their representation easily and can use it to explain the relationship between 30 groups of 6 and 30 groups of 3 whether they can use a different representation on the other *Student Activity Book* page.

SESSION FOLLOW-UP

3 Daily Practice

Daily Practice: For ongoing review, have students complete *Student Activity Book* page 21.

Student Math Handbook: Students and families may use *Student Math Handbook* pages 42, 43 for reference and review. See pages 176–181 in the back of this unit.

Assessment: Counting Around the Class

Math Focus Points

◆ Understanding the relationship among skip counting, counting repeated addition, and multiplication

◆ Understanding that doubling (or halving) one factor in a multiplication expression doubles (or halves) the product

Today's Plan		Materials
① DISCUSSION **Sharing Representations of the Multiples of 3 and 6**	🕐 20 MIN 👥 CLASS	• *Student Activity Book,* pp. 19–20 (completed)
② MATH WORKSHOP **Using Multiplication Combinations** **②A** Highlighting 100 Charts **②B** How Many Legs? **②C** Assessment: *Counting Around the Class*	🕐 40 MIN	**②A** • M12* • Colored pencils, markers, or crayons **②B** • *Student Activity Book,* p. 22 **②C** • M13*
③ SESSION FOLLOW-UP **Daily Practice and Homework**		• *Student Activity Book,* pp. 23–24 • *Student Math Handbook,* pp. 39, 40–41, 42

*See *Materials to Prepare,* p. 47.

Ten Minute-Math

Counting Around the Class Students count around the class by 4s. Each student says another multiple of 4 until all students have counted once. Highlight the multiples of 4 by writing them on the board as students say them.

How many students have counted at 24? 48? 80?

Can anyone think of a multiplication equation that would represent 6 people counting by 4s? ($6 \times 4 = 24$).

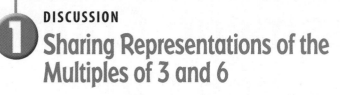

Algebra Note

① Properties of Multiplication As students consider the relationships between multiplying by 3 and 6, 5 and 10, or 4 and 8, they are investigating properties of multiplication. When students solve 30×3 by halving the product of 30×6, they are implicitly using an understanding of the meaning and characteristics of multiplication. One way of expressing this kind of reasoning in symbolic notation, using the associative property, is $30 \times 6 = 30 \times (3 \times 2) = (30 \times 3) \times 2$; (i.e., 30×6 is also twice 30×3). Students are not thinking formally about properties, but their reasoning is based on understanding that multiplication is an operation that involves equal groups: if the number of groups stays the same, but the number in each group is cut in half, the new product will be half the original product. See **Algebra Connections in This Unit,** p. 16.

Professional Development

② **Dialogue Box:** Bags of 6, Bags of 3, p. 171

DISCUSSION

20 MIN   CLASS

① Sharing Representations of the Multiples of 3 and 6

Math Focus Points for Discussion

◆ Understanding that doubling (or halving) one factor in a multiplication expression doubles (or halves) the product

Select two or three students to share their work from *Student Activity Book* pages 19–20. Focus the discussion on representations that show a relationship between 30 groups of 3 and 30 groups of 6. Ask questions such as the following, which are based on *Student Activity Book* page 20.**①**

Where are the groups of 3 in your picture (representation)? Where are the groups of 6? How did Ms. Ross know that she would need half as many apples when she filled her bags with three in each instead of six in each? How does your representation prove that she needs half as many apples?**②**

Students might say:

"I skip counted up by 3s to find out that she will need 90 apples to fill 30 bags. If each bag has six apples she will need 180, because each time you say a 6, you've gone up two 3s. 3 is half of 6 so she will need half as many apples."

"It is true that she will need 90 apples to fill 30 bags of 3 apples in each. This is because 3 is half of 6. If there were 31 kids in the class, you add 3 to 90 and get 93 and add 6 to 180 to get 186. 83 is still half of 186, so it is still true."

"I can show it on a number line. For each six apples she adds (one bag), she can make two bags of three apples. So 30 bags of three take half as many apples as 30 bags of six."

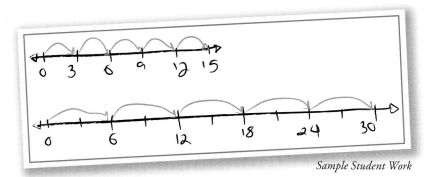

Sample Student Work

What if 30 students in Ms. Johnson's class counted around by 10s and then 5s? Would this relationship still be true? Would the thirtieth person get to a number twice as big when they count by 10 as when they count by 5? What do you think?

Some students may see this as a new problem with an unknown answer. Others may be able to explain that the number the thirtieth person says when counting by 10s will be twice as much as the number the thirtieth person says when counting by 5s because 5 is half of 10.

MATH WORKSHOP

40 MIN

2 Using Multiplication Combinations

Students work on the activities listed below during the remainder of this session and most of the next session. Make sure that all students spend time on the first activity.

2A Highlighting 100 Charts

PAIRS

Students work on charts for multiples of 4 and charts they have not finished. The goal is for each student to have a completed set of the multiples from 2–6 and 10.

Students who have time after they have completed the other activities work on multiples from 7–9 and 11.

For complete details about this activity, see Session 2.2, page 56.

❸ **Teacher Note:** Assessment: Counting Around the Class, p. 155

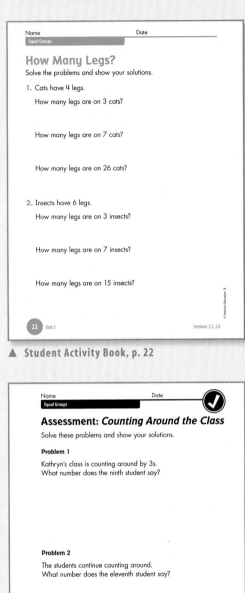

Name _____ Date _____
Equal Groups

How Many Legs?
Solve the problems and show your solutions.

1. Cats have 4 legs.

   How many legs are on 3 cats?

   How many legs are on 7 cats?

   How many legs are on 26 cats?

2. Insects have 6 legs.

   How many legs are on 3 insects?

   How many legs are on 7 insects?

   How many legs are on 15 insects?

22 Unit 5   Sessions 2.5, 2.6

▲ **Student Activity Book, p. 22**

Name _____ Date _____ ✔
Equal Groups

Assessment: Counting Around the Class

Solve these problems and show your solutions.

Problem 1

Kathryn's class is counting around by 3s.
What number does the ninth student say?

Problem 2

The students continue counting around.
What number does the eleventh student say?

Sessions 2.5, 2.6   Unit 5 M13

▲ **Resource Masters, M13** 📁 PORTFOLIO

Students discuss the patterns they find on multiples charts.

²ᴮ How Many Legs?
PAIRS

Students solve multiplication problems involving different numbers of legs on *Student Activity Book* page 22. These problems build up from small multiples (such as 3×4 and 7×4) to larger ones (such as 26×4). Encourage students to use what they know to solve the larger problems.

ONGOING ASSESSMENT: Observing Students at Work

Students use known combinations to solve larger multiplication problems.

- **Can students use smaller, known multiplication combinations to solve problems?** Can they determine how much of the problem they have solved and what is left to solve?

- **Are students gaining fluency with multiplication combinations?**

²ᶜ Assessment: *Counting Around the Class*
INDIVIDUALS

This assessment addresses Benchmark 2: Solve multiplication combinations and related division problems by using skip counting or known multiplication combinations. You will have another chance to assess students on this benchmark in the End-of-Unit Assessment.

In this assessment students solve two multiplication problems about counting around the class from Assessment: *Counting Around the Class* (M13). Have students work on their own, and collect their work as they finish. ❸

SESSION FOLLOW-UP

③ Daily Practice and Homework

Daily Practice: For ongoing review, have students complete *Student Activity Book* page 23.

Homework: On *Student Activity Book* page 24 students practice multiplying by 2s, 4s, and 8s.

Student Math Handbook: Students and families may use *Student Math Handbook* pages 39, 40–41, 42 for reference and review. See pages 176–181 in the back of this unit.

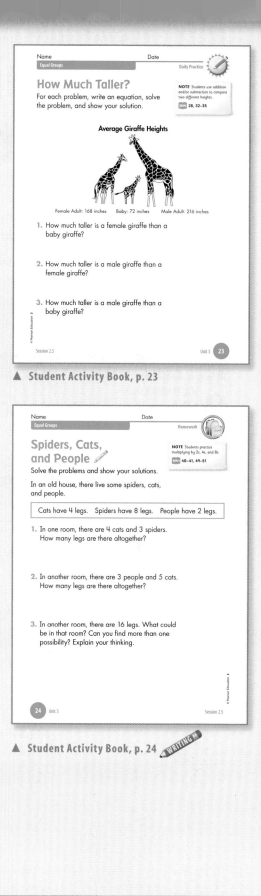

▲ Student Activity Book, p. 23

▲ Student Activity Book, p. 24

Using Multiplication Combinations

Math Focus Points

◆ Understanding the relationship between skip counting, repeated addition, and multiplication

◆ Understanding that doubling (or halving) one factor in a multiplication expression doubles (or halves) the product

◆ Using known multiplication combinations to determine the product of more difficult combinations

Today's Plan		Materials
MATH WORKSHOP **① Using Multiplication Combinations** **1A** Highlighting 100 Charts **1B** How Many Legs? **1C** Assessment: *Counting Around the Class*	🕐 40 MIN	**1A** • M12 (from Session 2.5) • Colored pencils, markers, or crayons **1B** • *Student Activity Book*, p. 22 (from Session 2.5) **1C** • M13 (from Session 2.5)
DISCUSSION **② Using What You Know**	🕐 20 MIN 👪 CLASS	• *Student Activity Book*, p. 22 (completed; from Session 2.5)
SESSION FOLLOW-UP **③ Daily Practice**		• *Student Activity Book*, p. 25 • *Student Math Handbook*, pp. 40–41, 42, 43, 44

Ten Minute-Math

Counting Around the Class Count around the class by a number you have already used this week. This may be a number that you feel students need to practice or one that was interesting to them in some way. While each student says a multiple of the chosen number, stop at various points and ask how many students have counted so far. When everyone has counted once, ask:

• How did you figure out the next number? Did you add? Did you follow a pattern?

MATH WORKSHOP
① Using Multiplication Combinations

40 MIN

Students continue with these Math Workshop activities from Session 2.5.

ⓐ Highlighting 100 Charts

PAIRS

Students work on charts they have not finished. The goal is for each student to have a completed set of the multiples from 2–6 and 10.

For complete details about this activity, see Session 2.2, page 56.

ⓑ How Many Legs?

PAIRS

For complete details about this activity, see Session 2.5, page 74.

ⓒ Assessment: *Counting Around the Class*

INDIVIDUALS

For complete details about this activity, see Session 2.5, page 74.

DISCUSSION
② Using What You Know

20 MIN   CLASS

Math Focus Points for Discussion

◆ Using known multiplication combinations to determine the product of more difficult combinations

Choose the final multiplication problem from the first set of problems on *Student Activity Book* page 22 and ask students to share their strategies for solving it. Record strategies as students share.

Let's focus on the final problem in the first set. You had to find how many legs are on 26 cats. How did you start? Just tell me your first step.

Collect the starting points, which should include a variety such as 2×4, 7×4, 10×4, or even 20×4. Then have students explain how they finished solving the problem, being sure to connect each step to the story context by focusing on how many legs so far, how many cats so far, and how many more cats until they have solved for all 26 cats.

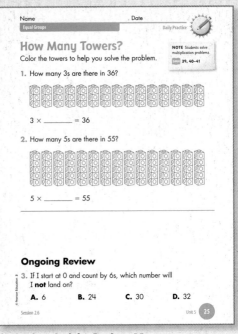

▲ **Student Activity Book, p. 25**

How did your first step help you? What had you figured out then? What did you do next to finish solving the problem?

Students might say:

 "I started with $10 \times 4 = 40$, so I have found out that there are 40 legs on ten cats. So ten more cats would have 40 legs, so $40 + 40 = 80$, which is 80 legs for 20 cats. Now I need six more cats. $6 \times 4 = 24$. So $80 + 24 = 104$. There are 104 legs on 26 cats."

 "I started with $2 \times 4 = 8$. So there are eight legs on two cats. I kept adding 8s until I had 13 groups of eight. That's 26 cats. 13 groups of eight equals 104."

Talk through a couple of different starts, one small (2×4) and one large (10×4), and encourage students to ask one another questions to clarify their strategies.

SESSION FOLLOW-UP

3 **Daily Practice**

 Daily Practice: For reinforcement of this unit's content, have students complete *Student Activity Book* page 25.

Student Math Handbook: Students and families may use *Student Math Handbook* pages 40–41, 42, 43, 44 for reference and review. See pages 176–181 in the back of this unit.

Mathematical Emphases

Whole Number Operations Understanding and working
with an array model of multiplication

Math Focus Points

- Using arrays to model multiplication situations

- Using arrays to find factors of 2-digit numbers up to 50

- Using arrays to identify characteristics of numbers, including prime and
square numbers

- Using arrays to find a product by skip counting by one of its dimensions

- Breaking an array into parts to find the product represented by the array

Computational Fluency Learning the multiplication
combinations with products up to 50 fluently

Math Focus Points

- Identifying and learning multiplication combinations not yet
known

- Using known multiplication combinations to determine the product
of more difficult combinations

Arrays

	Student Activity Book	Student Math Handbook	Professional Development: Read Ahead of Time	
SESSION 3.1 p. 82				
Arranging Chairs Students are introduced to arrays to represent multiplication. They use arrays to find factors and products.	26	45, 46	• **Teacher Note:** Representing Multiplication with Arrays, p. 157 • **Dialogue Box:** Arranging Chairs, p. 173	
SESSION 3.2 p. 87				
Investigating Arrays Students use arrays to find factors of numbers up to 50 and to identify features of numbers.	27	45, 46, 52, 53		
SESSION 3.3 p. 92				
Finding the Number of Squares in an Array Students use arrays to learn multiplication combinations with products up to 50 and to find factors of numbers up to 50.	28–29	45, 46	• **Dialogue Box:** Finding the Number of Squares in an Array, p. 174	
SESSION 3.4 p. 97				
Array Games—Part 1 Students learn an array game and continue using arrays to learn multiplication combinations with products up to 50 and to find factors of numbers up to 50.	31–33	45, 46; G10		
SESSION 3.5 p. 101				
Learning Multiplication Combinations Students generate strategies for learning multiplication combinations with which they are not yet fluent by relating them to combinations they do know.	31, 35–36	49–51; G19–G20	• **Teacher Note:** Learning Multiplication Combinations, p. 160	
SESSION 3.6 p. 107				
Array Games—Part 2 Students learn an array game and continue using arrays to learn multiplication combinations with products up to 50 and to find factors of numbers up to 50.	31, 37–38	46, 49–51; G9, G10		

Ten-Minute Math See page 18 for an overview.

What Time Is It?	Counting Around the Class
• Demonstration clock	• No materials needed
• Student clocks (1 per pair)	

Materials to Gather	Materials to Prepare
• **T62, Half-Inch Grid Paper** • **Connecting cubes** (12 for demonstration; 12 per student during demonstration) • **Connecting cubes** (30 per pair) • **Unlined colored paper** (2 sheets per pair) • **Scissors** (1 per student) • **Glue sticks** (1 per pair)	• **M14, Half-Inch Grid Paper** Make copies. (4 per pair) • **M15–M16, Arranging Chairs** Make copies. (1 per student) • **Number cards** Use the numbers 9, 15–21, 23–25, 27, 30. Write one number on each card. Make two sets.
• **Students' Arranging Chairs posters** (from Session 3.1) • **Scissors** (1 per student) • **Resealable plastic bags** (1 per student)	• **M17–M24, Array Cards** (students' sets) Make copies. (1 set per student) • **M25, How to Make Array Cards** (1 per student) • **T63–T70, Array Cards** Cut apart. Store in an envelope or plastic sleeve in the binder for future use.
• **T63–T70 Transparency Array Cards** (2 of each) • **Chart paper** • **Arranging Chairs materials** See Session 3.1. • **Making Array Cards materials** See Session 3.2.	• **Chart paper** Write a list of the numbers up to 50 not yet on display.
• **T71, "Combinations I Know /Combinations I'm Working On"** • **Array Cards** (1 set per pair) • **Arranging Chairs materials** See Session 3.1.	• **M26, *Factor Pairs*** Read the rules in advance Make copies. (as needed) • **T63–T70 Transparency, Array Cards** Choose any four cards. • **Class list of Numbers for Arrays** Update the list. • **M27, "Combinations I Know" and "Combinations I'm Working On"** Make copies. (as needed)
• **Array Cards** (1 set per pair) • **Envelopes or resealable plastic bags** (1 per student) • **Paper clips** (1 per student) • **Scissors** (1 per student)	• **Chart paper** Divide the chart paper into two columns and label them "Combinations We're Working On" and "Start With." • **M28–M33, Multiplication Cards** Make copies. (1 set per student) • **M34–M35, *Practicing with Multiplication Cards*** Make copies. (1 per student) • **M37–M38, Family Letter** Make copies. (1 per student)
• **Array Cards** (1 set per pair) • **Materials for *Factor Pairs*** See Session 3.4. • **Materials for Making Multiplication Cards** See Session 3.5.	• **M36, *Count and Compare*** Make copies. (as needed) • **T63–T70, Array Cards** Round 1: any 2 cards; Round 2: 3×4 and 2×6; Round 3: 6×6, 7×5

 Overhead Transparency

Arranging Chairs

Math Focus Points

◆ Using arrays to model multiplication situations

◆ Using arrays to find factors of 2-digit numbers up to 50

Vocabulary

dimension

Today's Plan		Materials
ACTIVITY **① Introducing Arranging Chairs**	20 MIN CLASS INDIVIDUALS	• M14*; T62 • Connecting cubes
ACTIVITY **② Arranging Chairs**	40 MIN PAIRS	• M14*; M15–M16* • Number cards for Arranging Chairs*; connecting cubes; unlined colored paper; scissors ; glue sticks
SESSION FOLLOW-UP **③ Daily Practice**		• *Student Activity Book,* p. 26 • *Student Math Handbook,* pp. 45, 46

*See *Materials to Prepare,* p. 81.

Ten-Minute Math

What Time Is It? Write 2:12 on the board and have students show the time on their clocks.

How did you know where to put the small hand? How about the big hand? How many minutes is it past 2:00? What two five-minute interval times is it in between?

(2:10 and 2:15)

Ask additional similar questions using these times: 10:03, 3:36, and 11:17.

ACTIVITY

1 Introducing Arranging Chairs

20 MIN **CLASS** **INDIVIDUALS**

Begin this session by placing 12 cubes on the overhead projector.

Here's a problem called "Arranging Chairs." Imagine that these 12 cubes are chairs and that you need to arrange them in straight rows for an audience to watch a class play. You want to arrange the chairs so that there will be the same number in every row with no chairs left over. How many different ways could you do this? How many chairs would be in each row? How many rows would there be? Try different ways to arrange the chairs, even if some of the ways don't seem very good for watching a class play.

Give students time to make as many different arrangements as they can, using their 12 cubes. When students have finished, ask them to describe their arrays.❶

How many rows are in the arrangement you made? How many chairs are in each row?

Discuss two possible arrangements with the class. As you do so, model the use of the words **dimension** and **by**.

[Jung] arranged her chairs in two rows with six chairs in each row. I am going to draw this as a rectangle. Each square stands for 1 chair, so two rows of six squares stand for [Jung]'s two rows of six chairs. The dimensions of her rectangle are 2 by 6. [Benjamin] made three rows with four chairs in each row. What are the dimensions of his rectangle?❷

Students give dimensions for arrays.

Professional Development

❶ **Teacher Note:** Representing Multiplication with Arrays, p. 157

Math Note

❷ **Multiplication Notation for Arrays** The *Investigations* curriculum uses the convention of designating the number of rows first and the number in each row second; for example, 3 × 2 indicates three rows with two in each row.

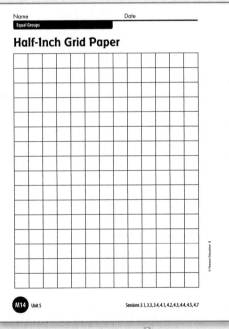

▲ **Resource Masters, M14; T62**

Now show all of the possible arrangements by drawing and labeling them on Half-Inch Grid Paper (T62), on large graph paper, or on the board. List the multiplication equations that describe each rectangle underneath. Explain that each set of dimensions is a pair of factors for that number.❸

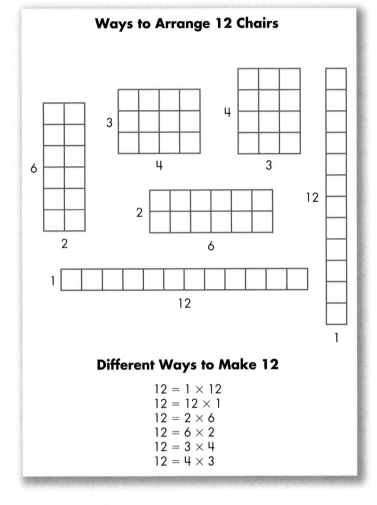

Ways to Arrange 12 Chairs

Different Ways to Make 12

$$12 = 1 \times 12$$
$$12 = 12 \times 1$$
$$12 = 2 \times 6$$
$$12 = 6 \times 2$$
$$12 = 3 \times 4$$
$$12 = 4 \times 3$$

② ACTIVITY

Arranging Chairs

40 MIN   PAIRS

Give each pair of students two of the number cards you prepared before the session. Make sure that at least two pairs of students work on the same number so that they can compare their work.

Each pair of students should use cubes to find all possible arrays for one of their numbers and draw the arrays they find on Half-Inch Grid Paper (M14). Students should then cut out all the arrays they found for their number, glue them onto a piece of colored paper, and write the title "Ways to Arrange [their number] Chairs." They should label the dimensions of each array and list the dimensions underneath, following the directions on Arranging Chairs (M15–M16). Pairs who are working on the same number can meet together to compare their answers. Students follow the same procedure for their second number.❹

As students work, connect the pairs of dimensions for their arrays to factors. For example, when students are listing the dimensions for 18, you may say:

I see you found all of the pairs that multiply to 18.

As students complete their arrangements, hang their posters in a classroom display. Tell students to look at all of the posters when they have finished their work and to think about what they notice.❺

ONGOING ASSESSMENT: Observing Students at Work

Through building arrays, students find the factors of given numbers to 30.

- **How do students find the arrangements that work?** What knowledge of equal groups do they have? For example, do they know that they can make two rows for any even number? Are there other multiplication combinations that they know?

- **Do students recognize that, if they can make an arrangement with two rows of a number, then they can also make that number of rows of two?** In other words, do they know that if they can make a 2 × 8 array, they can also make an 8 × 2 array?

- **Do they use one arrangement to figure out others, or do they randomly move the cubes around until they find a new arrangement?**

Professional Development
❹ **Dialogue Box:** Arranging Chairs, p. 173

Algebra Note

❺ **Commutative Property** Students may notice that some of the factor pairs are reversals of each other; that is, if 3 × 4 is on the list, so is 4 × 3. Students are noticing examples of the commutative property. When students comment on this property, ask why they think these reversals occur. Is the same thing true with other pairs of factors? Encourage students to examine their models to see why multiplication has this property. For more information, see **Algebra Connections in This Unit** on page 16.

Name _____ Date _____

Equal Groups

Arranging Chairs (page 1 of 2)

You need
- 30 cubes
- 4 sheets of half-inch grid paper
- Scissors
- Glue stick
- 2 sheets of unlined colored paper

Work with a partner.

1. Write the first number you are working on. _____

2. Figure out all the ways you can arrange that many chairs. Each row of each arrangement must have the same number of chairs. Show your arrangements as rectangles.

3. Draw each rectangle on the grid paper.

4. Cut out each rectangle and glue it onto the colored paper. Label each rectangle with its dimensions.

5. Make a list of the dimensions you found for your number. Your paper should look like the one on M16.

6. Write the second number you are working on and follow steps 2–5. _____

Sessions 3.1, 3.2, 3.3, 3.4   Unit 5 **M15**

▲ Resource Masters, M15

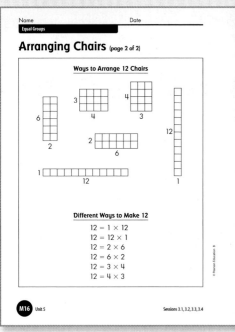

▲ Resource Masters, M16

▲ Student Activity Book, p. 26

Intervention Questioning students who are arranging cubes randomly will help them slow down and think through their approach.

- I see that you made an arrangement for your number with four rows. Look at what you have. Is there any way that you can put some rows together or split them up in order to make a different arrangement? Can you make a rectangle for your number with two rows?

- You made a rectangle of four rows with six in each row. Can you make a rectangle with six rows? How many would be in each row then?

- Think about 24 for a minute. What are some ways that you might be able to split up 24?

Extension Some students may be able to work with larger numbers. Ask these students to arrange 64, 72, or 128 chairs.

SESSION FOLLOW-UP
3 Daily Practice

 Daily Practice: For ongoing review, have students complete *Student Activity Book* page 26.

 Student Math Handbook: Students and families may use *Student Math Handbook* pages 45, 46 for reference and review. See pages 176–181 in the back of this unit.

Investigating Arrays

Math Focus Points

◆ Using arrays to identify characteristics of numbers, including prime and square numbers

◆ Using arrays to find factors of 2-digit numbers up to 50

Vocabulary

array
square number
prime number

Today's Plan		Materials
DISCUSSION ① **Sharing Our Arrays**	20 MIN CLASS	• Students' Arranging Chairs posters (from Session 3.1)
ACTIVITY ② **Making Array Cards**	40 MIN CLASS INDIVIDUALS	• M17–M24*; M25*; T63–T70* • Scissors; resealable plastic bags
SESSION FOLLOW-UP ③ **Daily Practice**		• *Student Activity Book*, p. 27 • *Student Math Handbook*, pp. 45, 46, 52, 53

*See *Materials to Prepare*, p. 81.

Ten-Minute Math

What Time Is It? Write 8:24 on the board and have students show that time on their clocks.

How did you know to set the time on your clock?

How do you say the time?

What two five-minute interval times is 8:24 in between? (8:20 and 8:25)

Ask additional similar questions using these times: 4:33, 9:01, and 12:58.

Name _____ Date _____
Equal Groups

Array Cards (page 1 of 8)

✂

Sessions 3.1, 3.2, 3.3, 3.4, 3.5, 3.6, 4.1, 4.2, 4.3, 4.5, 4.6, 4.7   Unit 5 **M17**

▲ Resource Masters, M17–M18; T63–T64

DISCUSSION

① Sharing Our Arrays

20 MIN   CLASS

Math Focus Points for Discussion

◆ Using arrays to find factors of 2-digit numbers up to 50

◆ Using arrays to identify characteristics of numbers, including prime and square numbers

Make sure that all students have had time to look at the classroom display of the Arranging Chairs posters from Session 3.1. Then start the discussion by telling students that items grouped in equal rows to form rectangles are called arrays.

What did you notice as you looked at the arrays that people made for their numbers?

Students might say:

"Some numbers made lots of arrays, and others made only 2 or 3."

"Every number made a long, skinny array that has rows of 1 or just one row. Some numbers made only long, skinny arrays—17 made only a 1 by 17 array and a 17 by 1 array."

"Some numbers made square arrays, and others did not. Some numbers had an even number of arrays, and others had an odd number."

As students share their observations, introduce the concept of square numbers by asking questions such as the following:

[Pilar] noticed that some numbers made square arrays and others didn't. What numbers made square arrays? What else did you notice about these numbers? What other numbers do you think would make square arrays? ①

Students may notice that only these numbers have an odd number of arrays because the square arrangement (e.g., 4 × 4) has no partner in the way all other arrangements do (e.g., 2 × 8 and 8 × 2). Let students know that numbers with a square array are called square numbers.

Now introduce the concept of prime numbers by asking questions such as the following:

[Denzel] noticed that 17 cubes made only a 1 by 17 array and a 17 by 1 array. What other numbers made only two arrays? [Kathryn] says 19. What are the factors of 19? What about this poster for 23? What are its factors?

Let students know that numbers with only two factors, the number itself and 1, are called prime numbers.

Now ask students about numbers that have many arrays.

[Elena] noticed that some numbers made many arrays and others made only a few. Did the largest numbers have the most arrays? What if we look at 24 and 25—which one had more arrays? What do you think would happen if we tried some even larger numbers, such as 56 or 99 or 100? Do you think there are prime numbers larger than 23?

Some students may enjoy investigating such questions by finding factors of larger numbers during the remainder of this unit.

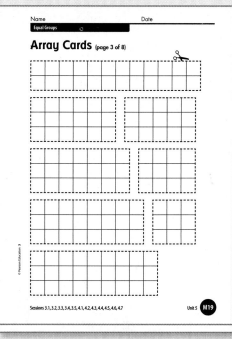

▲ Resource Masters, M19–M20; T65–T66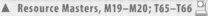

ACTIVITY

2 Making Array Cards

40 MIN   CLASS   INDIVIDUALS

The eight pages of Array Cards (M17–M24) provide 51 arrays representing multiplication combinations in the 2 to 12 tables with products up to 50. In this activity, students make their own set of cards by following the directions on How to Make Array Cards (M25).

Introduce the process of cutting out and labeling the cards, using your set of transparency Array Cards (T63–T70) to demonstrate.

Start by placing the transparency Array Cards from the second sheet (T64) on the overhead.

Tell students to look at the transparency Array Cards cut from the sheet and explain that they will be making their own set by carefully cutting out each individual array in their sheet, following the outlines of the grid as exactly as possible. Explain that seeing the exact outline of each array is important for the array games they will be playing.

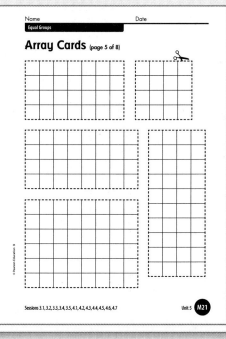

▲ Resource Masters, M21–22; T67–T68

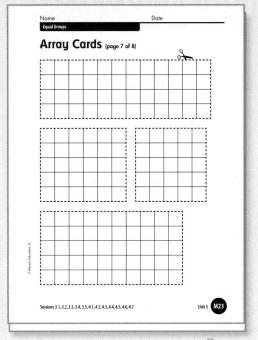

Name _____ Date _____
Equal Groups
Array Cards (page 7 of 8)

Sessions 3.1, 3.2, 3.3, 3.4, 3.5, 4.1, 4.2, 4.3, 4.4, 4.5, 4.6, 4.7   Unit 5 **M23**

▲ Resource Masters, M23–M24; T69–T70

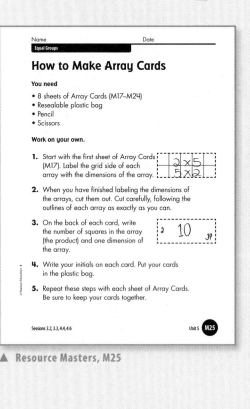

Name _____ Date _____
Equal Groups

How to Make Array Cards

You need
• 8 sheets of Array Cards (M17–M24)
• Resealable plastic bag
• Pencil
• Scissors

Work on your own.

1. Start with the first sheet of Array Cards (M17). Label the grid side of each array with the dimensions of the array.

2. When you have finished labeling the dimensions of the arrays, cut them out. Cut carefully, following the outlines of each array as exactly as you can.

3. On the back of each card, write the number of squares in the array (the product) and one dimension of the array.

4. Write your initials on each card. Put your cards in the plastic bag.

5. Repeat these steps with each sheet of Array Cards. Be sure to keep your cards together.

Sessions 3.2, 3.3, 4.4, 4.6   Unit 5 **M25**

▲ Resource Masters, M25

Remove all but the 2 × 5 and 5 × 2 transparency grid from the overhead and have students locate the same grid on their copies of Array Cards (M18) (top right). Write the dimensions of the array on your overhead grid, and have students do the same on their grids.

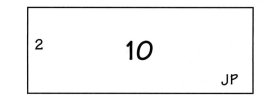

Show students how to label the back of the array card. Trace the array on the blank transparency to draw a rectangle representing the back of the array card. Write the number of squares in the array (the product represented by the array). Tell students that they will be doing this on their grid after they cut it out later in the session. Explain that they are to check the number with a classmate or someone at home before they write it permanently.

Choose one of the dimensions of the array and write it and the product on the other side as shown. Write your initials in the bottom right corner. Tell students that they will be doing this later in the session.

```
2              10
                       JP
```

Have students label all of the grids on the first sheet of Array Cards (M17), cut them out, and complete the backs, following the directions on How to Make Array Cards (M25). Tell them to move on to the second sheet of Array Cards (M18) and so on until the set is finished. Have them store all of their cards in the plastic bag.

Students needing more time can work on completing the cards in the Session 3.3 Math Workshop.

ONGOING ASSESSMENT: Observing Students at Work

Students label the dimensions and products on a set of array cards.

As students are working, help them figure out what to do and how to label each card.

• **How do students find the number of squares in each array?**
  Do they count the squares by 1s or do they skip count by the number in a column or row? Do they use known multiplication combinations to help them find the number of squares in each array?

- **Do students use the number of squares of other arrays they have done to help them figure out the number of squares in a new array?** For example, do they use the fact that an 8 × 4 array has 32 squares to figure out that a 9 × 4 array has 36 squares (32 + 4)?

DIFFERENTIATION: Supporting the Range of Learners

Intervention It is likely that you will find some students counting the squares on their arrays by ones. Suggest that these students try other ways of finding the product represented by the array. Ask questions such as the following:

- Can you think of a faster way to count the squares on this array?

- Can skip counting help you figure out the total number of squares in this array? What number(s) can you skip count by?

- Are there multiplication combinations you know that might help you figure out the number of squares? For example, a student trying to figure out the number of squares in a 6 × 5 array might know the answer to the multiplication combination 5 × 5 and could simply add another row of 5 to get the total.

SESSION FOLLOW-UP

③ Daily Practice

Daily Practice: For ongoing review, have students complete *Student Activity Book* page 27.

Student Math Handbook: Students and families may use *Student Math Handbook* pages 45, 46, 52, 53 for reference and review. See pages 176–181 in the back of this unit.

Name _____ Date _____
Equal Groups   Daily Practice

Crossing Over 100

Solve the following sets of related problems. Think about how to use one problem to solve the next one.

NOTE Students practice solving subtraction problems in related sets.
SMH 32–35

1. 100 − 68 = _____ 110 − 68 = _____ 120 − 68 = _____	**2.** 100 − 74 = _____ 112 − 74 = _____ 132 − 74 = _____
3. 100 − 94 = _____ 113 − 94 = _____ 123 − 94 = _____	**4.** 100 − 43 = _____ 110 − 43 = _____ 120 − 43 = _____
5. 100 − 37 = _____ 120 − 37 = _____ 124 − 37 = _____	**6.** 100 − 81 = _____ 130 − 81 = _____ 136 − 81 = _____

© Pearson Education 3

Session 3.2   Unit 5   27

▲ **Student Activity Book, p. 27**

Finding the Number of Squares in an Array

Math Focus Points

◆ Using arrays to find a product by skip counting by one of its dimensions

◆ Breaking an array into parts to find the product represented by the array

◆ Identifying and learning multiplication combinations not yet known

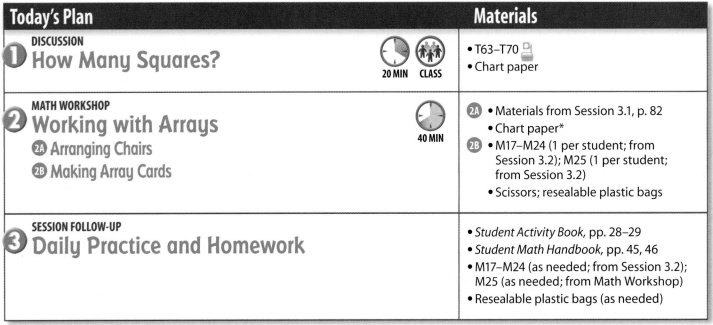

Today's Plan		Materials
DISCUSSION **① How Many Squares?**	20 MIN CLASS	• T63–T70 • Chart paper
MATH WORKSHOP **② Working with Arrays** **2A** Arranging Chairs **2B** Making Array Cards	40 MIN	**2A** • Materials from Session 3.1, p. 82 • Chart paper* **2B** • M17–M24 (1 per student; from Session 3.2); M25 (1 per student; from Session 3.2) • Scissors; resealable plastic bags
SESSION FOLLOW-UP **③ Daily Practice and Homework**		• *Student Activity Book,* pp. 28–29 • *Student Math Handbook,* pp. 45, 46 • M17–M24 (as needed; from Session 3.2); M25 (as needed; from Math Workshop) • Resealable plastic bags (as needed)

*See *Materials to Prepare,* p. 81.

Ten-Minute Math

What Time Is It?   Say the time 1:33 and ask students to write it. Then, students show the time on their clocks. Be sure that students show 33 minutes past 1:00 on their clocks. Ask students to write and model the following times on their clocks: 10:21, 4:27, and 3:13.

DISCUSSION

How Many Squares?

20 MIN   **CLASS**

Professional Development

❶ Dialogue Box: Finding the Number of Squares in an Array, p. 174

Math Focus Points for Discussion

◆ Using arrays to find a product by skip counting by one of its dimensions

◆ Breaking an array into parts to find the product represented by the array

Start this session with a discussion of different ways to determine the number of squares in an array. Place the transparency of the 4 × 6 array on the overhead.

Who has a way to figure out the number of squares in this 4 × 6 array?

Have volunteers come up to the front of the class and demonstrate their ideas on the overhead projector. Some students will count by 1s, counting each individual square. Others will count by 4s or by 6s.❶

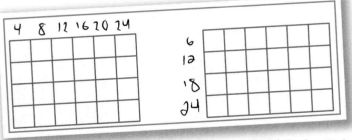

Sample Student Work

As students share their strategies, write them on chart paper with an example for each. Post the list for students to refer to as they continue the activities in this session and the next. Now remind students of the meaning of the word *product*.

When you find the total number of squares in an array, you are finding the product. The product is the answer to a multiplication problem. Who has a different way of finding the number of squares, or the product, of an array that does not involve counting the squares by ones or skip counting by the number in each row or column?

Focus on the strategy of using familiar combinations to determine the number of squares in an array by calling on students whom you observed using this strategy.

Students might say:

"I know that 2 × 6 = 12, so 4 × 6 must be 24."

"I know that 3 × 6 = 18. I have to add one more 6. 18 plus 6 equals 24."

[Gina] knows that 2 × 6 equals 12, so a 2 × 6 array has 12 squares in all. Where is the 2 × 6 part of this 4 × 6 array? [Gina] knows that this part, 2 rows of 6, is 12. What is the other part of the array? [Nicholas] said that 3 × 6 equals 18 and used that to figure out the squares in 4 × 6. Where is the 3 × 6 part of the 4 × 6 array? What part of the array is left?

To help the class understand the strategy of using known combinations, some students show their methods by using the arrays on the overhead projector.

If the strategy of using familiar multiplication combinations does not come up from students, raise it yourself. Ask students whether there are any smaller arrays within the larger one for which they can easily find the total. For example, many students will know the multiplication combination 2 × 6. Pointing to the array, raise a question such as the following:

Let's look at 2 rows of this array—2 rows of 6. How can that help you find the number of squares in the whole 4 × 6 array?

Collect a few examples.

MATH WORKSHOP

Working with Arrays

40 MIN

In this Math Workshop, students find factors of numbers up to 50 and work with multiplication combinations with products up to 50. Students who need to finish making their array cards should begin with that activity.

2A Arranging Chairs

PAIRS

For complete details about this activity, see Session 3.1, page 83. Tell students to choose their own numbers from the set of number cards for this activity. Add students' completed posters to the classroom display of arrays.

DIFFERENTIATION: Supporting the Range of Learners

Extension Challenge students to look for square numbers and prime numbers. Have them make a list of each type of number in their math journals and write about any patterns that they notice for the series of square numbers.

2B Making Array Cards

INDIVIDUALS

For complete details about this activity, see Session 3.2, page 89.

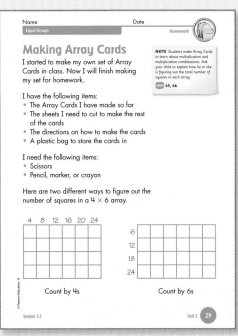

Name

Date

Equal Groups

Daily Practice

How Many More?

Solve the problems. Show your solutions on the number lines.

NOTE Students find the missing number to make an addition equation correct.

29

1. 112 + _____ = 250

2. 58 + _____ = 275

3. 137 + _____ = 300

4. 146 + _____ = 320

28 Unit 5

Session 3.3

▲ Student Activity Book, p. 28

Name

Date

Equal Groups

Homework

Making Array Cards

I started to make my own set of Array Cards in class. Now I will finish making my set for homework.

NOTE Students make Array Cards to learn about multiplication and multiplication combinations. Ask your child to explain how he or she is figuring out the total number of squares in each array

45, 46

I have the following items:
• The Array Cards I have made so far
• The sheets I need to cut to make the rest of the cards
• The directions on how to make the cards
• A plastic bag to store the cards in

I need the following items:
• Scissors
• Pencil, marker, or crayon

Here are two different ways to figure out the number of squares in a 4 × 6 array.

4   8   12   16   20   24

Count by 4s

6
12
18
24

Count by 6s

Session 3.3

Unit 5 29

▲ Student Activity Book, p. 29

SESSION FOLLOW-UP

3 Daily Practice and Homework

 Daily Practice: For ongoing review, have students complete *Student Activity Book* page 28.

Homework: Students needing more time to finish cutting out and labeling their Array Cards do so for homework. For these students, send home *Student Activity Book* page 29, their Array Card sheets (M17–M24), their copy of the directions (M25), the cards they have cut out so far, and their plastic storage bag.

If the cards are to be a classroom set, tell students to bring them back to class tomorrow. If they are a set to keep at home, tell students to store them in a convenient place where they can find them easily when they need them for homework use.

You may want to have all students bring back their cards to give you the opportunity to check their work.

Student Math Handbook: Students and families may use *Student Math Handbook* pages 45, 46 for reference and review. See pages 176–181 in the back of this unit.

Array Games – Part 1

Math Focus Points

- Using arrays to find a product by skip counting by one of its dimensions
- Identifying and learning multiplication combinations not yet known
- Using known multiplication combinations to determine the product of more difficult combinations

Today's Plan		Materials
① ACTIVITY **Introducing *Factor Pairs***	20 MIN CLASS	• *Student Activity Book,* p. 31 • T63–T70 ; T71 • Array Cards
② MATH WORKSHOP **Array Games – Part 1** **②A** Playing *Factor Pairs* **②B** Arranging Chairs	40 MIN	**2A** • *Student Activity Book,* p. 31 • M26 (as needed)*; M27 (as needed)* • Array Cards **2B** • M14*; M15* • Number cards for Arranging Chairs; connecting cubes; unlined colored paper; scissors; glue sticks
③ SESSION FOLLOW-UP **Daily Practice and Homework**		• *Student Activity Book,* pp. 31–33 • *Student Math Handbook,* pp. 45, 46; G10 • M26*; M27 (as needed)* • Array Cards

*See *Materials to Prepare,* p. 81.

Ten-Minute Math

Counting Around the Class Ask students questions about an imaginary class that is counting by 2s.

When the class had finished counting, the last number was 44. How many students are in that class?

What number did the 5th person say?

What number did the 10th person say?

What number would they get to if they counted around *again*?

For each question, collect answers as well as explanations about how students found their answers.

① Introducing *Factor Pairs*

The array game *Factor Pairs* is designed to help students learn their multiplication combinations with products up to 50. Introduce the game to the class.

This year, our goal is for everyone in the class to know the products of all of the multiplication combinations on your Array Cards. One way to help us do this is to play a game called *Factor Pairs*. This game will help us use the combinations we know to find the ones we don't know.

Put four transparency Array Cards (T63–T70) on the overhead projector and explain that you are placing them dimensions side up. Choose a volunteer to be your partner as you play two sample rounds. As you are teaching students the game, point out ways that they can find solutions if they get stuck.

If you get stuck in finding the product, think of the strategies we discussed for finding the number of squares in an array. For example, you pick an array with the dimensions 7×3. How can you use skip counting to figure out the number of squares? How can you use the product of 7×2 to help you figure out the number of squares in the 7×3 array?

Display "Combinations I Know" and "Combinations I'm Working On," (T71) on the overhead projector. Tell students that they will use *Student Activity Book* page 31 to list the multiplication combinations they know and those they are learning. Have a brief discussion of what it means to know a multiplication combination. Contrast multiplication combinations such as 2×2 and 2×3, which most students know, with a more difficult combination such as 8×6 by asking questions such as the following:

If I ask you what 2×2 is, you can probably tell me that the answer is 4 without really having to think about it. When you are playing *Factor Pairs*, 2×2 will probably go on your list of "Combinations I Know." If you pick an array with the dimensions 8×6, most of you will use one of your strategies to figure out the number of squares in the array. For example, you might skip count by 8 or 6, or you might use a smaller array within the big one to help you figure out the total. 8×6 will probably go on your list of "Combinations I'm Working On" because you don't know it right away.❶

Differentiation

❶ **English Language Learners** You can demonstrate the word *automatically* while previewing this activity with English Language Learners. Show two array cards—one showing a known combination and one showing a more challenging one. [Kenji,] which combination is easy for you? What's the answer? I can tell you know that one *automatically* because you answered so quickly. Let's write it under "Combinations I Know." Which combination is harder for you? Let's write that one under "Combinations I'm Working On." You can keep practicing that combination until it's easy and *automatic*, like the first one. Observe English Language Learners as they play the game, assessing whether they are recording the combinations on the correct lists and using appropriate strategies to solve the challenging combinations.

Name _____ Date _____

Equal Groups

"Combinations I Know" and "Combinations I'm Working On"

As you play *Factor Pairs*, make a list of the multiplication combinations you know and the ones that you are still working on. This list will change as you learn more of the combinations.

Combinations I Know	Combinations I'm Working On

Sessions 3.4, 3.5, 3.6   Unit 5 31

▲ **Student Activity Book, p. 31; Resource Masters, M27; T71**

For the next ten minutes, all students play the game in pairs. Use this time to observe students to make sure that they understand the directions and to determine which students will need support during the Math Workshop that follows. You may want to have a few extra copies of the rules available, which can be found on *Factor Pairs* (M26).

MATH WORKSHOP

40 MIN

2 Array Games—Part 1

Students choose between two activities to help them find factors of numbers up to 50 and learn multiplication combinations with products up to 50. Students will have the opportunity to work on *Factor Pairs* again in Session 3.6.

2A Playing *Factor Pairs*

PAIRS

Students play *Factor Pairs* with a partner, using one set of Array Cards.

ONGOING ASSESSMENT: Observing Students at Work ✓

Students work on determining the products represented by arrays when given the dimensions of the arrays.

- **How are students figuring out the products represented by the array cards?** Are they skip counting? Are they using multiplication combinations that they know?

- **What multiplication combinations are most students familiar with?** Which combinations are still hard for most students?

DIFFERENTIATION: Supporting the Range of Learners

Intervention For students having difficulty, ask questions such as the following, which are based on the 5 × 7 Array Card:

- How will you figure out how many squares there are altogether?

- Can you skip count by 5 (or 7)? How will that help?

- Is there a multiple of 5 (or 7) that you already know that will get you partway there (for example, 10 or 14)?

- Can you see any smaller multiplication combinations that you know are within the big array?

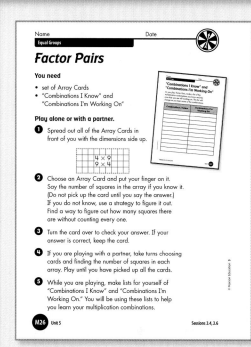

▲ Resource Masters, M26

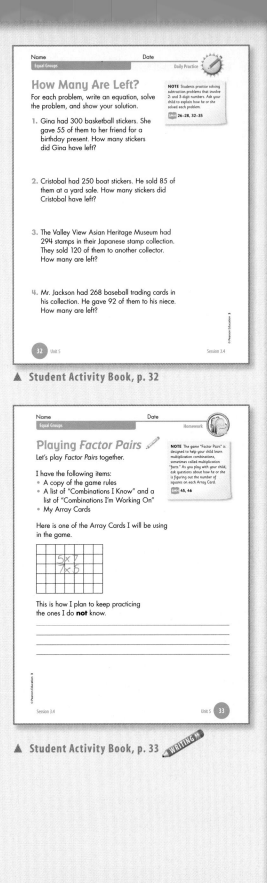

▲ Student Activity Book, p. 32

▲ Student Activity Book, p. 33

Questioning students as they work can encourage them to develop more efficient strategies that are based on knowledge they have of multiplication relationships.

2B Arranging Chairs

PAIRS

For complete details about this activity, see Session 3.1, page 84. Tell students to choose their own numbers from the set of number cards for this activity. Add students' completed posters to the classroom display of arrays.

SESSION FOLLOW-UP

3 Daily Practice and Homework

 Daily Practice: For ongoing review, have students complete *Student Activity Book* page 32.

 Homework: Students continue to play *Factor Pairs* for homework. Send home *Student Activity Book* page 33, a copy of the game rules (M26), their lists of "Combinations I Know" and "Combinations I'm Working On" (*Student Activity Book* page 31, and M27 as needed). Also send home sets of students' Array Cards if they do not have them at home. Tell students to keep the copy of the rules at home.

Student Math Handbook: Students and families may use *Student Math Handbook* pages 45, 46 and G10 for reference and review. See pages 176–181 in the back of this unit.

Learning Multiplication Combinations

Math Focus Points

◆ Identifying and learning multiplication combinations not yet known

◆ Using known multiplication combinations to determine the product of more difficult combinations

Today's Plan		Materials
DISCUSSION **① Using Known Multiplication Combinations**	20 MIN CLASS	• *Student Activity Book,* p. 31 (from Session 3.4) • Chart paper*
ACTIVITY **② Making Multiplication Cards**	40 MIN INDIVIDUALS PAIRS	• *Student Activity Book,* p. 31 (from Session 3.4) • M28–M33*; M34–M35* • Array Cards; envelopes or resealable plastic bags; paper clips; scissors
SESSION FOLLOW-UP **③ Daily Practice and Homework**		• *Student Activity Book,* pp. 35–36 • M28–M33 (optional)*; M34–M35*; M37–M38, Family Letter* • *Student Math Handbook,* pp. 49–51; G19–G20

*See *Materials to Prepare,* p. 81.

Ten-Minute Math

Counting Around the Class Ask students questions about an imaginary class that is counting by 5s.

When the class had finished counting, the last number was 90.

How many students are in the class?

What number did the 5th person say?

What number did the 10th person say?

What number would they get to if they counted around again?

For each question, collect answers as well as explanations about how students found their answer.

① Distributive Property Strategies like these are based on the *distributive property,* which relates the operations of multiplication and addition. Applying this property, the product of a multiplication expression such as 9×4 can be found by breaking up one of the factors. For example, $9 \times 4 = (5 \times 4) + (4 \times 4)$ or $9 \times 4 = (10 \times 4) - (1 \times 4)$. It is not important for students to name this property. They will, however, be applying it as they develop strategies to solve the problems in this unit and in later grades. For more information about the distributive property, read "Algebra Connections in This Unit" on page 16.

DISCUSSION

① Using Known Multiplication Combinations

20 MIN CLASS

Math Focus Points for Discussion

◆ Using known multiplication combinations to determine the product of more difficult combinations

Remember that our goal is for all of you to know the product of each multiplication combination in your Array Card set. Let's make a list of some of the pairs that are hard to remember and think about ways we can help one another learn them.

On the chart paper you prepared, under the heading "Combinations We're Working On," make a list of students' responses. Then choose one of the multiplication combinations mentioned by several students.

Several people said that 9×4 is a hard combination to remember. Is there another combination with 4 or 9 as a factor that you know that can help you figure out the product of 9×4?

Students might say:

"I think of 9×4 as $(10 \times 4) - 4$. I know that 10×4 is 40. If I take away one 4, then 9×4 is 36."

"I thought about 9×4 as an array. I know that 2 rows of 9 equals 18. Another 9×2 is 18, and 18 plus 18 is 36."

"I first solved $5 \times 4 = 20$ because I knew that in my head. Then I solved $4 \times 4 = 16$. $20 + 16 = 36$."

Record students' responses on chart paper under the "Start With" heading across from the 9×4 combination. Each time a student suggests a starting combination, ask what the next step would be and record this as well.

Let's look at the example that breaks 9×4 into $(5 \times 4) + (4 \times 4)$. What is a story that shows how this equals 9×4?①

Listen for stories similar to the following:

To find out how many wheels are on nine cars, do a few cars at a time. Five cars have 20 wheels. Now use four more cars to make nine cars. Four cars have 16 wheels. 20 plus 16 is 36, so 9 times 4 equals 36.

A few of you thought that 6×5 is a hard combination to remember. What other multiplication combinations do you know that can help you solve this one?

Emphasize that, although there are many starting places for solving each multiplication combination, students should think about ones that they can use easily because the idea is to find the solution quickly. Record a few starting places for this combination, and then post the chart where students can return to it, both for reference and to record clues for other combinations as they review and practice over the next few sessions.

Students suggest strategies for learning difficult multiplication combinations.

ACTIVITY

2 Making Multiplication Cards

40 MIN   INDIVIDUALS   PAIRS

Tell students that they will be doing three things for the rest of math class: making a set of Multiplication Cards (M28–M33),❷ ❸ using the cards to find the combinations they need to work on, and writing a clue on each of these cards that will help them find the product.

Here's an example. Let's say that 6×5 is one of the cards you are working on. Is there a combination that you already know that might help you find the product?

Math Notes

❷ **Multiplication Cards** The Multiplication Cards in Grade 3 include all the multiplication cards with products up to 50 except for the combinations including 0 and 1 because it is expected that students know these already.

❸ **Multiplying by 0** Students are sometimes confused when they encounter multiplying by 0. It may be useful to start with other multiplication combinations that students know, put them in a context, and then extend the context to multiplication by zero. For example, if I have two apples in each of five bags, I have ten apples ($5 \times 2 = 10$); if I have one apple in each of five bags, I have five apples ($5 \times 1 = 5$); if I have zero apples in each of the five bags, I have zero apples ($5 \times 0 = 0$). Students can visualize or act out these situations. Ask them to consider situations that can be represented by 5×0 as well as situations that can be represented by 0×5 (the latter can be more difficult for students to understand). Students can think of a situation for 0×5 or reason from their understanding of the commutative property of multiplication that if $5 \times 0 = 0$, then $0 \times 5 = 0$.

Name _____ Date _____

Equal Groups

Multiplication Cards (page 1 of 6)

2×2	2×3 3×2
Start with _____	Start with _____
2×4 4×2	2×5 5×2
Start with _____	Start with _____
2×6 6×2	2×7 7×2
Start with _____	Start with _____
2×8 8×2	2×9 9×2
Start with _____	Start with _____

M28 Unit 5   Sessions 3.5, 3.6, 4.2, 4.3, 4.5, 4.6

▲ **Resource Masters, M28–M33**

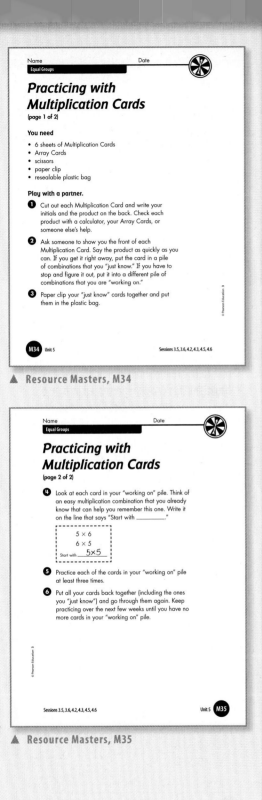

▲ Resource Masters, M34

▲ Resource Masters, M35

Students might say:

"I know 6 × 5 because I know my 5s. 5 × 5 = 25. But I need one more 5. 25 + 5 = 30."

"I know 2 × 6 = 12. 12 + 12 = 24. That is 4 groups of 6. I need one more 6. 24 + 6 = 30."

"I could use 3 × 5 = 15 and double that to get 6 × 5. 15 + 15 = 30."

Draw the following Multiplication Card front and back on the board:

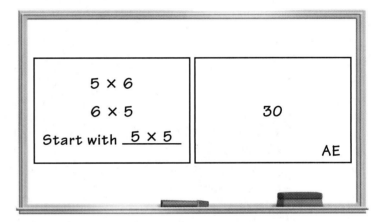

The front of the Multiplication Card for 6 × 5 might look like this [point to the front]. You will write the product [point to 30] on the back. When you are finished making your set of cards, you will see which ones you already know and which ones you need to learn. You may be surprised to realize that you already know quite a few of these! Here's an example: What is the answer to 2 × 4? 3 × 2? 5 × 3? If you can say the answer in a couple of seconds, you put those cards into your "just know" pile. If it takes you a little while to figure out the answer, put the card in your "working on" pile.

Working with a partner, students follow the directions on *Practicing with Multiplication Cards* (M34–M35).

Students should be encouraged to repeat the practice routine with the cards in their "working on" pile when they have a few minutes, either outside of math time or during math when they have completed another task. Let them know that their goal over the next few months is to have all of the multiplication combinations with products to 50 "at their fingertips" as they work on multiplication problems with larger numbers. ④

ONGOING ASSESSMENT: Observing Students at Work

Students use multiplication combinations they know to help them solve and learn combinations with which they are not yet fluent.

- **With which multiplication combinations are students fluent?** ⑤ Are they fluent with 2s, 5s, and 10s?

- **Can students solve one multiplication combination by relating it to another?** For example, can they find 4×6 by doubling 2×6 or by thinking of 3×11 as $(3 \times 10) + 3$?

DIFFERENTIATION: Supporting the Range of Learners

Intervention Help students having difficulty coming up with "start with" factor pairs by going through their "just know" facts with them. Consider, for example, $\times 4$ combinations. Help them see that 6×4 is the same as adding one more group of 4 to the combination 5×4 that they know. Encourage them to use Array Cards, skip counting charts, and/or cubes to examine the relationship between 5×4 and 6×4, and ask questions such as the following:

- What $\times 4$ combinations that you "just know" are close to $\times 4$ combinations that you're "working on"?

- I see that you know 5×4, but you are still working on 6×4. How can 5×4 help you figure out 6×4?

Professional Development

④ **Teacher Note:** Learning Multiplication Combinations, p. 160

Math Note

⑤ **Fluency** By the end of Grade 3, students are expected to know fluently the multiplication combinations with products up to 50 (Set A of the Array Cards). As the year continues, students should continue practicing with their multiplication cards and playing array games to gain fluency. Support for this will be provided in upcoming units as homework and practice pages. Students will be assessed on their fluency with the multiplication combinations up to a product of 50 in Unit 8, *How Many Hundreds? How Many Miles?*

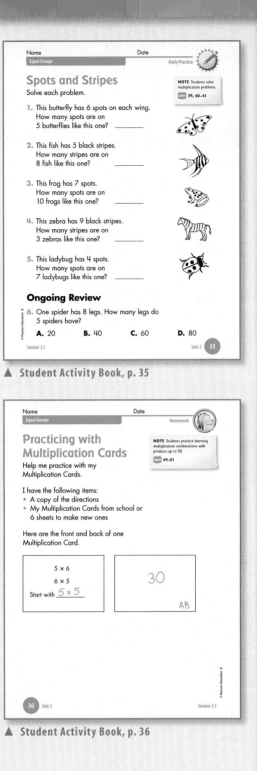

▲ Student Activity Book, p. 35

▲ Student Activity Book, p. 36

③ Daily Practice and Homework

 Daily Practice: For reinforcement of this unit's content, have students complete *Student Activity Book* page 35.

Homework: Students continue to practice with their Multiplication Cards for homework. Send home *Student Activity Book* page 36, a copy of the directions, *Practicing with Multiplication Cards* (M34–M35), and their sets of Multiplication Cards or copies of the cards (M28–M33) if they will be making a second set. Tell students to keep the copy of the directions (and their Multiplication Cards if they are a second set) at home.

Student Math Handbook: Students and families may use *Student Math Handbook* pages 49–51 and G19–G20 for reference and review. See pages 176–181 in the back of this unit.

Family Letter: Send home copies of the Family Letter (M37–M38).

Array Games—Part 2

Math Focus Points

◆ Breaking an array into parts to find the product represented by the array

◆ Identifying and learning multiplication combinations not yet known

◆ Using known multiplication combinations to determine the product of more difficult combinations

Today's Plan		Materials
ACTIVITY **① Introducing *Count and Compare***	20 MIN CLASS	• M36 (as needed)*; T63–T70 • Array Cards
MATH WORKSHOP **② Array Games—Part 2** **②A** Playing *Count and Compare* **②B** Making Multiplication Cards **②C** Playing *Factor Pairs*	40 MIN	**②A** • M36 (as needed)* • Array Cards **②B** • Materials from Session 3.5, p. 101 **②C** • *Student Activity Book,* p. 31 (from Session 3.4) • M26 • Array Cards
SESSION FOLLOW-UP **③ Daily Practice and Homework**		• *Student Activity Book,* pp. 37–38 • *Student Math Handbook,* pp. 46, 49–51; G9; G10 • M36*; Array Cards (as needed)

*See *Materials to Prepare,* p. 81.

Ten-Minute Math

Counting Around the Class Count around the class by a number you have already used this week. This may be a number that you think students need to practice or one that was interesting to them in some way. While each student says a multiple of the chosen number, stop at various points and ask how many students have counted so far. When everyone has counted once, ask:

• How did you figure out the next number? Did you add? Did you follow a pattern?

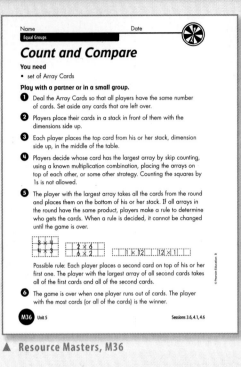

Name _____ Date _____

Equal Groups

Count and Compare

You need
• set of Array Cards

Play with a partner or in a small group.

❶ Deal the Array Cards so that all players have the same number of cards. Set aside any cards that are left over.

❷ Players place their cards in a stack in front of them with the dimensions side up.

❸ Each player places the top card from his or her stack, dimension side up, in the middle of the table.

❹ Players decide whose card has the largest array by skip counting, using a known multiplication combination, placing the arrays on top of each other, or some other strategy. Counting the squares by 1s is not allowed.

❺ The player with the largest array takes all the cards from the round and places them on the bottom of his or her stack. If all arrays in the round have the same product, players make a rule to determine who gets the cards. When a rule is decided, it cannot be changed until the game is over.

Possible rule: Each player places a second card on top of his or her first one. The player with the largest array of all second cards takes all of the first cards and all of the second cards.

❻ The game is over when one player runs out of cards. The player with the most cards (or all of the cards) is the winner.

M36   Unit 5   Sessions 3.6, 4.1, 4.6

▲ **Resource Masters, M36**

ACTIVITY

❶ Introducing *Count and Compare*

Count and Compare is a game that provides practice with multiplication combinations and encourages thinking about the relationship between size, shape, and dimensions. The game is played by groups of two or three players with a single set of array cards divided evenly among them.

Play a few rounds with the whole class. You can use *Count and Compare* (M36) to make extra copies of the rules.

Begin by placing two transparency Array Cards (T63–T70) with the same product (such as a 3 × 4 and a 2 × 6) on the overhead projector. Explain that, when this happens, the players decide together who will get the cards; for example, each player places another card down and the one with the larger product takes all four cards.

Next, choose two arrays that are close in size (such as a 6 × 6 and a 7 × 5), and project them side-by-side.

These two arrays are close in size. How can you figure out which array is bigger?

Students might suggest comparing the areas by looking at them, but this kind of direct comparison is difficult and can be misleading when the arrays are close in size. Encourage students to skip count, to use known combinations, or to place one array on top of the other. Tell them that counting by 1s is not allowed.

Students suggest strategies for determining the larger array.

Make sure that students understand that they determine which array is larger without turning them over to look at the product side. Explain that they not only need to determine which array is bigger but must also give a reason why.

Tell students that play continues until one player runs out of cards. The array cards can then be reshuffled (with the leftovers) and dealt out for a new game.

For the next ten minutes, all students play the game. Use this time to observe students to make sure that they understand the directions to the game and to determine which students will need support during the Math Workshop that follows.

MATH WORKSHOP

40 MIN

2 Array Games—Part 2

Students engage in activities that help them find factors of numbers up to 50 and learn multiplication combinations with products to 50.

2A Playing *Count and Compare*

PAIRS **GROUPS**

Students play *Count and Compare* with a partner or in small groups.

ONGOING ASSESSMENT: Observing Students at Work

Students practice multiplication combinations and think about relationships between size, shape, and dimensions by comparing two arrays and determining which has the bigger product.

- **With which multiplication combinations are students developing fluency?**

- **What strategies are students using to determine the bigger array when two arrays appear close in size?**

- **Are students recognizing that arrays that have different shapes can have the same product?** For example, do they see that a 3×12 array, a 6×6 array, and a 4×9 array all have a product of 36?

Students' strategies may vary, depending on the relative sizes of the two arrays in each round. When two arrays seem close in size (for example, a 6×7 array and a 5×8 array), students will need strategies other than determining the larger array visually. Refer students to the class list of strategies for finding the total of an array.

2B Making Multiplication Cards

INDIVIDUALS

For complete details about this activity, see Session 3.5, page 103. Students who have not yet completed the set of cards they started in Session 3.5 should do so in this session.

2C Playing *Factor Pairs*

PAIRS

For complete details about this activity, see Session 3.4, page 99. Put students' completed *Student Activity Book* page 31 into their portfolios.

SESSION FOLLOW-UP

3 Daily Practice and Homework

Daily Practice: For ongoing review, have students complete *Student Activity Book* page 37.

Homework: Students play *Count and Compare* and *Factor Pairs* for homework. Send home *Student Activity Book* page 38 and a copy of the game rules for *Count and Compare* (M36). They should already have copies of the game rules for *Factor Pairs* (M26) and their lists of "Combinations I Know" and "Combinations I'm Working On" at home. Also send home sets of Array Cards if students do not have them at home. Tell students to keep the copy of the rules for *Count and Compare* at home.

Student Math Handbook: Students and families may use *Student Math Handbook* pages 46, 49–51 and G9, G10 for reference and review. See pages 176–181 in the back of this unit.

Left margin worksheet images

Name _____ **Date** _____
Equal Groups — Daily Practice

Make $1.00, Make $2.00

NOTE Students practice finding combinations of numbers that add up to a given total.

1. Fill in the blanks to make combinations of four amounts that add up to $1.00.

Example:

$0.25 + $0.25 + $0.40 + $0.10 = $1.00

_____ + $0.12 + _____ + _____ = $1.00

_____ + _____ + $0.13 + _____ = $1.00

_____ + $0.33 + _____ + _____ = $1.00

2. Fill in the blanks to make combinations of four amounts that add up to $2.00.

_____ + $0.35 + _____ + _____ = $2.00

_____ + _____ + $0.36 + _____ = $2.00

_____ + _____ + _____ + $0.41 = $2.00

Session 3.6 — Unit 5 37

▲ **Student Activity Book, p. 37**

Name _____ **Date** _____
Equal Groups — Homework

Playing Array Games

Let's play *Count and Compare* together.

NOTE The new game "Count and Compare" is designed to help your child learn multiplication combinations, sometimes called multiplication facts. As you play with your child, ask questions about how he or she is figuring out the number of squares on each Array Card. Also revisit the array game "Factor Pairs," which you and your child have already played together.

SMH 49–51

I have the following items:
• A copy of the game rules
• A list of "Combinations I Know" and a list of "Combinations I'm Working On"
• My Array Cards

Let's play *Factor Pairs* together.

I have the following items:
• A copy of the game rules
• My Array Cards

Here are some of my Array Cards that we will be playing with.

3 × 4
4 × 3

2 × 6
6 × 2

1 × 12   12 × 1

38 Unit 5 — Session 3.6

▲ **Student Activity Book, p. 38**

Mathematical Emphases

Whole-Number Operations Understanding the meaning of multiplication

Math Focus Points

◆ Writing and solving multiplication problems in context

◆ Using and understanding multiplication notation

◆ Understanding multiplication as combining equal groups

◆ Understanding the relationship among skip counting, repeated addition, and multiplication

Computational Fluency Learning the multiplication combinations and products up to 50 fluently

Math Focus Points

◆ Identifying and learning multiplication combinations not yet known

Whole-Number Operations Developing strategies for division based on understanding the inverse relationship between multiplication and division

Math Focus Points

◆ Understanding division as the splitting of a quantity into equal groups

◆ Using the inverse relationship between multiplication and division to solve problems

◆ Using multiplication combinations to solve division problems

◆ Using and understanding division notation

◆ Writing and solving division problems in context

Understanding Division

	Student Activity Book	Student Math Handbook	Professional Development: Read Ahead of Time	
SESSION 4.1 p. 116				
Solving Division Problems Students solve a set of division story problems and share their approaches for solving them.	39–41	47, 48; G9	• **Teacher Note:** The Relationship Between Multiplication and Division, p. 148 • **Teacher Note:** Two Kinds of Division: Sharing and Grouping, p. 163	
SESSION 4.2 p. 121				
Multiply or Divide? By solving story problems, students examine the difference between multiplication and division situations.	42–44	47, 48; G19–G20	• **Dialogue Box:** Is It Multiplication or Division?, p. 175	
SESSION 4.3 p. 125				
Writing Story Problems Students examine the relationship between multiplication and division. They write story problems for a class multiplication and division book.	45	39, 40–41, 47, 48; G19–G20		
SESSION 4.4 p. 129				
Missing Factors Students learn and play *Missing Factors,* a game in which they identify the missing dimension of an array when given the number of squares and one dimension.	46–47	39, 47, 48; G17–G18		
SESSION 4.5 p. 133				
Solving Multiplication and Division Problems Students work on activities in a Math Workshop designed to develop their understanding of the inverse relationship between multiplication and division.	48	39, 40–41, 47, 48, 49–51; G17–G18, G19–G20		

Materials to Gather	Materials to Prepare
• **Posters: Things that Come in 2s, 3s, 4s, and so on** (from Investigation 1) • **Students' multiples charts** (from Investigation 2; as needed) • **Array Cards** (as needed) • **Connecting cubes** (as needed)	• **M14, Half-Inch Grid Paper** Make copies. (as needed) • **M36,** *Count and Compare* Make copies. (as needed)
• **M39, Multiplication and Division Chart** (optional) • **Students' multiples charts** (from Investigation 2; as needed) • **Array Cards** (as needed) • **Multiplication Cards** (as needed) • **Connecting cubes** (as needed)	• **M14, Half-Inch Grid Paper** Make copies. (as needed) • **M34–M35,** *Practicing with Multiplication Cards* Make copies. (as needed) • **Chart paper** Divide the paper into four columns. Label the columns "Number of groups," "Number in Each Group," "Product," and "Equation."
• **Students' multiples charts** (from Investigation 2) • **Array Cards** (as needed) • **Students' Multiplication Cards** (as needed) • **Connecting cubes** (as needed) • **Unlined paper** (2 sheets per student)	• **M14, Half-Inch Grid Paper** Make copies. (as needed) • **M34–M35,** *Practicing with Multiplication Cards* Make copies. (as needed)
• **T73,** *Missing Factors* **Recording Sheet** 🖨 • **Students' multiples charts** (from Investigation 2; as needed) • **Array Cards** (as needed) • **Connecting cubes** (as needed)	• **M14, Half-Inch Grid Paper** Make copies. (as needed) • **T72,** *Missing Factors* **Arrays** 🖨 Cut apart transparency arrays. Store in an envelope or plastic sleeve in the binder for future use. • **M41–M42,** *Missing Factors* Make copies. (as needed) • **M43,** *Missing Factors* **Recording Sheet** Make copies. (1 per student)
• **Students' multiples charts** (from Investigation 2) • **Array Cards** (as needed) • **Multiplication Cards** (as needed) • **Connecting cubes** (as needed) • **Class Multiplication/Division Books**	• **M14, Half-Inch Grid Paper** Make copies. (as needed) • **M27, "Combinations I Know/Combinations I'm Working On"** Make copies. (1 per student) • **M34–M35,** *Practicing with Multiplication Cards* Make copies. (as needed) • **M41–M42,** *Missing Factors* Make copies. (as needed) • **M43,** *Missing Factors* **Recording Sheet** Make copies. (1 per student)

🖨 Overhead Transparency

Understanding Division,
continued

	Student Activity Book	Student Math Handbook	Professional Development: Read Ahead of Time	
SESSION 4.6 p. 137				
Solving Multiplication and Division Problems, *continued* Students continue to work on activities in a Math Workshop designed to develop their understanding of the inverse relationship between multiplication and division.	49	39, 40–41, 47, 48, 49–51; G9, G17–G18, G19–G20		
SESSION 4.7 p. 141				
End-of-Unit Assessment Students solve two problems to assess their understanding of multiplication and division.	50	39, 40–41, 47, 48, 49–51	• **Teacher Note:** End-of-Unit Assessment, p. 165	

Materials to Gather	Materials to Prepare
• **Students' multiples charts** (from Investigation 2) • **Array Cards** (as needed) • **Multiplication Cards** (as needed) • **Connecting cubes** (as needed)	• **M14, Half-Inch Grid Paper** Make copies. (as needed) • **M27, "Combinations I Know/Combinations I'm Working On"** Make copies. (1 per student) • **M34–M35,** *Practicing with Multiplication Cards* Make copies. (as needed) • **M36,** *Count and Compare* Make copies. (1 per pair/group) • **M41–M42,** *Missing Factors* Make copies. (as needed) • **M43,** *Missing Factors* **Recording Sheet** Make copies. (1 per student) • **Class Multiplication/Division Book** Make copies of students' problems from Session 4.3. (1 per student)
• **Students' multiples charts** (from Investigation 2) • **Array Cards** (as needed) • **Connecting cubes** (as needed)	• **M14, Half-Inch Grid Paper** Make copies. (as needed) • **M44, End-of-Unit Assessment** Make copies. (1 per student)

Solving Division Problems

Math Focus Points

◆ Understanding division as the splitting of a quantity into equal groups

◆ Using the inverse relationship between multiplication and division to solve problems

Vocabulary

division

Today's Plan		Materials
ACTIVITY ① **Solving Division Story Problems** 40 MIN INDIVIDUALS PAIRS		• *Student Activity Book,* pp. 39–40 • M14 (as needed)* • Posters of Things That Come in Groups (from Investigation 1); students' multiples charts (from Investigation 2; as needed); cubes (as needed); Array Cards (as needed)
DISCUSSION ② **Sharing Our Solutions** 20 MIN CLASS		• *Student Activity Book,* pp. 39–40 (completed)
SESSION FOLLOW-UP ③ **Daily Practice and Homework**		• *Student Activity Book,* p. 41 • M36 (as needed)*; Array Cards (as needed) • *Student Math Handbook,* pp. 47, 48; G9

*See *Materials to Prepare,* p. 113.

Ten-Minute Math

What Time Is It? Write 5:38 on the board and ask students to show the time on their clocks.

How did you know to show the time on the clock?

Can you say the time aloud?

Do you know that it can also be read 22 minutes before 6:00?

What two five-minute interval times is it in between? (5:35 and 5:40)

Ask additional similar questions using times that are in between five-minute intervals, such as 10:09, 5:17, and 11:43.

ACTIVITY

① Solving Division Story Problems

40 MIN   INDIVIDUALS   PAIRS

In this session, students solve a set of division story problems. Before assigning the problems, model a similar one with the class.

I am going to choose something from our list of "Things That Come in Groups" to make a problem for you to solve. This problem is going to be different from the ones we have been solving.

Read the following story problem aloud:

Frogs usually have four legs. In a pond, there are 16 legs altogether. How many frogs are in the pond?

Tell students to work with a partner to solve the problem. Have them think about what is the same or different about this problem and the ones they have been solving and writing recently. Have available such tools as Half-Inch Grid Paper (M14), cubes, students' highlighted multiples charts from Investigation 2, and students' Array Cards for those students who want to use them in this session and all other sessions in Investigation 4.

After a few minutes, collect a few strategies. Students should be able to solve the problem in several ways: drawing a picture and assigning legs to frogs until they have 16 total; skip counting up to 16 by 4s; or reasoning by using a combination they know (I know that two frogs have eight legs, so four frogs have 16 legs because $8 + 8 = 16$).

What is the same or different about this problem and the ones we have been solving and writing for the past few weeks?

Some students may notice that this problem is about equal groups, as are all of the multiplication problems. Other students may be able to explain that, in this problem, you start with the total and separate it into equal groups, whereas in the other problems you started with the groups and found the total. Students may identify the earlier problems as multiplication and these as division.❶

After collecting a few ideas, move on to the problems on *Student Activity Book* pages 39–40.❷ ❸ Have students work in pairs, encouraging them to share ideas and approaches as they work.

Professional Development

❶ **Teacher Note:** The Relationship Between Multiplication and Division, p. 148

❸ **Teacher Note:** Two Kinds of Division: Sharing and Grouping, p. 163

Math Note

❷ **Grouping vs. Sharing** The problems on these pages represent two types of division situations; Problem 1 is a *grouping* problem in which 28 desks are divided into groups of four desks each, and Problem 2 is a *sharing* problem in which 18 trading cards are shared equally among three friends. Students do not need to know the terms, but they should recognize both as division situations, be able to visualize each situation, and be able to identify what information is given and what information they have to figure out.

Name _____ Date _____

Equal Groups

Division Stories (page 1 of 2)

Solve each of the problems below and show your solution clearly.

1. There are 28 desks in the classroom. The teacher puts them in groups of 4. How many groups of desks are in the classroom?

2. Three friends are given a pack of trading cards to share equally. The pack contains 18 cards. How many cards should each person get?

© Pearson Education 3

Session 4.1   Unit 5   39

▲ **Student Activity Book, p. 39**

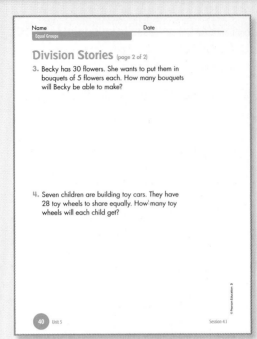

Name Date

Equal Groups

Division Stories (page 2 of 2)

3. Becky has 30 flowers. She wants to put them in bouquets of 5 flowers each. How many bouquets will Becky be able to make?

4. Seven children are building toy cars. They have 28 toy wheels to share equally. How many toy wheels will each child get?

40 Unit 5 Session 4.1

© Pearson Education 3

▲ Student Activity Book, p. 40

Students use any math tools they find helpful to solve division story problems.

ONGOING ASSESSMENT: Observing Students at Work

Students solve division story problems and represent their solutions.

- **Can students solve the division problems?**
- **What approaches are students using to solve these problems?** Are they skip counting, using related multiplication pairs, or using cubes?

DIFFERENTIATION: Supporting the Range of Learners

Intervention Help students model the action of these problems. To focus on starting with a quantity and dividing that quantity into equal groups, ask questions such as the following, which are based on Problem 1:

- What information do you know about this problem?
- Can you use cubes to represent the chairs?
- How many groups of 4 can you make with 28 cubes?

ELL The use of cubes or other visuals will help English Language Learners understand these problems if the vocabulary used to describe them is unfamiliar. You may also want to make a list of the common questions that are repeated in this assignment, such as How many will be in each *group?* How many does each *person* get? How many *groups* will there be? If English Language Learners understand these questions, it will be easier for them to understand the discussions that follow about knowns and unknowns and whether each story presents a multiplication or division situation.

Math Note

❹ **Solution Strategies** Expect to hear a range of approaches. Some students may directly model the problem by starting with 28 cubes and dealing them out into groups of 4, either one at a time or in groups. Some may draw tallies (or another representation of the chairs) and then circle and count groups of 4. Some may count by 4 until they reach 28. Others may start with a known multiplication combination such as 5 × 4.

DISCUSSION

② Sharing Our Solutions

20 MIN   CLASS

Math Focus Points for Discussion

◆ Understanding division as the splitting of a quantity into equal groups

◆ Using the inverse relationship between multiplication and division to solve problems

Write Problem 1 from *Student Activity Book* page 39 on the board or on chart paper and have a volunteer read it aloud to the class.

What information is given in this problem? What did you need to find out? How did you solve the problem?❹

As students share their approaches, ask questions to help reinforce that this situation involves dividing 28 desks into groups of 4 desks each.

• [Edwin] counted by 4 until he got to 28. Why did he do that? How many times did he count by 4?

• [Kathryn] started with 28 cubes and divided them into groups of 4 cubes each. Why did she do that? How many groups did she make?

• [Chiang] used a multiplication combination that she knew, 5 × 4, to help her solve this problem. How many desks are in 5 groups of 4? How many desks did she have left to divide into groups of 4?

At the end of the discussion, explain to students that the story problems they solved were all division problems. Each division problem gives a total that must be divided into equal groups. The answer is the number of groups or the number of items in each group. For example, students started with a total of 28 desks and broke them up into groups of 4 desks. The question they answered was how many groups of desks there were.

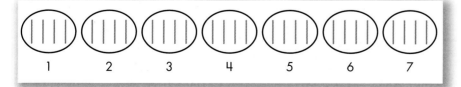

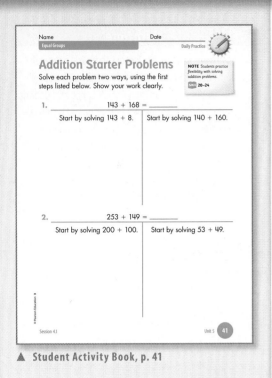

Name _____ Date _____
Equal Groups

Addition Starter Problems

Daily Practice

Solve each problem two ways, using the first steps listed below. Show your work clearly.

NOTE Students practice flexibility with solving addition problems.
SMH 20–24

1.   143 + 168 = _____

| Start by solving 143 + 8. | Start by solving 140 + 160. |

2.   253 + 149 = _____

| Start by solving 200 + 100. | Start by solving 53 + 49. |

© Pearson Education 3

Session 4.1   Unit 5   41

▲ **Student Activity Book, p. 41**

SESSION FOLLOW-UP

3 Daily Practice and Homework

 Daily Practice: For ongoing review, have students complete *Student Activity Book* page 41.

 Homework: Students continue to play *Count and Compare* for homework, using the rules they have at home. Send home additional copies of the rules (M36) as needed. Also, send home Array Cards if they do not have a home set.

 Student Math Handbook: Students and families may use *Student Math Handbook* pages 47, 48 and G9 for reference and review. See pages 176–181 in the back of this unit.

Multiply or Divide?

Math Focus Points

◆ Using the inverse relationship between multiplication and division to solve problems

◆ Using multiplication combinations to solve division problems

◆ Using and understanding division notation

Today's Plan		Materials
ACTIVITY **① Solving Story Problems** 40 MIN · INDIVIDUALS · PAIRS		• *Student Activity Book,* pp. 42–43 • M14 (as needed)* • Students' multiples charts (from Investigation 2; as needed); cubes (as needed); Array Cards (as needed)
DISCUSSION **② Multiply or Divide?** 20 MIN · CLASS		• M39 (optional) • Chart paper*
SESSION FOLLOW-UP **③ Daily Practice and Homework**		• *Student Activity Book,* p. 44 • M34–M35 (as needed)* • Multiplication Cards (as needed) • *Student Math Handbook,* pp. 47, 48; G19–G20

*See *Materials to Prepare,* p. 113.

Ten-Minute Math

What Time Is It? Write 11:18 on the board and ask students to show that time on their clocks. Ask students:

• How did you know to show the time on the clock?

• Can you say the time aloud?

• Do you know that it can also be read as 18 minutes past 11:00?

• What two five-minute interval times is it in between? *(11:15 and 11:20)*

Ask additional similar questions using times that are between five-minute intervals, such as 7:58, 9:14, and 3:09.

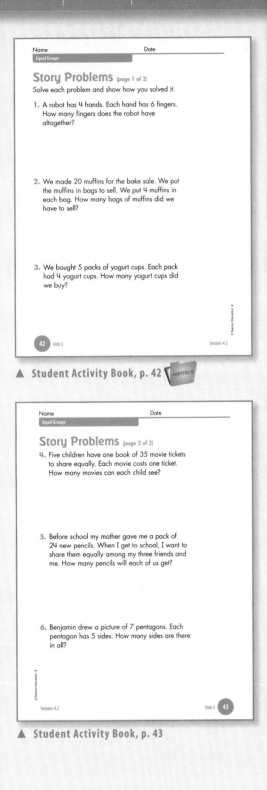

▲ Student Activity Book, p. 42

▲ Student Activity Book, p. 43

ACTIVITY
1 Solving Story Problems

40 MIN INDIVIDUALS PAIRS

In this session, students solve multiplication and division problems. Before assigning the problems, discuss how to determine which type of problem each is. Write Problem 1 from *Student Activity Book* pages 42 on the board or on chart paper and have a volunteer read it aloud to the class.

Describe this problem. What do you know and what are you trying to find out?

Highlight for students that this problem identifies the number of groups and the number of items that are in each group. Because they need to find how many are there altogether, this is a multiplication problem.

Have students work on their own or in pairs to solve this problem and the rest of the problems on *Student Activity Book* pages 42–43, using any method that makes sense to them. Remind students working together that each one should record his or her solutions individually.

Encourage students to act out the action of each problem, using cubes or drawings. Doing so will help students recognize that the division situations have them starting with an amount that gets divided into equal groups.

ONGOING ASSESSMENT: Observing Students at Work

Students solve six story problems that represent either multiplication or division situations.

- **Can students answer the questions in each story problem?**

- **What strategies are students using to solve the division problems on the student sheet?**

DISCUSSION
2 Multiply or Divide?

20 MIN CLASS

Math Focus Points for Discussion

◆ Using the inverse relationship between multiplication and division to solve problems

Bring the students together to discuss Problems 2 and 3. Write these problems on the board so that everyone can see them both.

What is the same about these problems? What is different? What information do you know in Problem 2? What about Problem 3? What do we call each of these types of problems?

Listen for students to identify Problem 2 as a division problem because we are told the total number of muffins and are asked to find how many equal bags can be made. Problem 3 is a multiplication problem because we are told how many packs of yogurts were bought and are asked to find how many cups were bought altogether. Some students may notice that the numbers are the same in both problems.

Explain to students that the division for Problem 2 can be shown in two ways. Write both ways on the board.❶

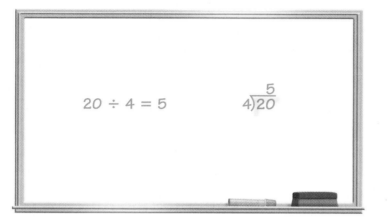

Let's think about Problem 2. How did you solve it?❷

Students might say:

 "I counted by 4 five times until I got to 20—4, 8, 12, 16, 20—so I know that there are five bags of muffins."

 "I started with 20 cubes and kept making groups of 4. I made 5 groups, so the answer is 5 bags of muffins."

 "I know that 5 times 4 equals 20. So 5 bags of 4 muffins would make 20 muffins."

Display the chart paper that you divided into columns from Multiplication and Division Chart (M39). Have the class help you fill in the information for Problem 2, writing the known information for the problem and putting

Math Note

❶ **Standard Notations for Division** It is important that students learn to recognize standard notations for multiplication and division. In this Investigation, the division notation $20 \div 4$ is used. Students should also become familiar with the notation $4\overline{)20}$. Help students interpret both notations meaningfully so that they can find the quotient on the basis of their understanding of the number relationships in the problem. In this case, how many groups of 4 are in 20? Throughout this investigation and the rest of the year, use these notations so that students become familiar with them.

Professional Development

❷ **Teacher Note:** Two Kinds of Division: Sharing and Grouping, p. 163

Name _____ Date _____
Equal Groups

Multiplication and Division Chart

Number of Groups	Number in Each Group	Product	Equation

Session 4.2   Unit 5 M39

▲ Resource Masters, M39

Professional Development

❸ Dialogue Box: Is It Multiplication or Division?, p. 175

▲ Student Activity Book, p. 44

---

a question mark in the "Number of Groups" column. Then ask for a volunteer to fill in the last column on the chart with the equation that describes the problem.

Follow the same procedure for Problem 3. Students should recognize that the unknown information for this problem is the product (the number of yogurt cups in all). Once again, have a volunteer write an equation that best represents the problem. Let students know that this chart will remain posted as a reference as they move to writing multiplication and division problems in the next session.❸

Number of Groups	Number in Each Group	Product	Equation
?	4 muffins	20	$20 \div 4 =$ ____ or ____ $\times 4 = 20$
5 packs	4 yogurt cups	?	$5 \times 4 =$ ____

SESSION FOLLOW-UP

③ Daily Practice and Homework

 Daily Practice: For reinforcement of this unit's content, have students complete *Student Activity Book* page 44.

Homework: Students continue to practice with their Multiplication Cards for homework, using the directions they have at home. Send home additional copies of the directions (M34–M35) as needed. Also, send home students' Multiplication Cards if they do not have a home set.

Student Math Handbook: Students and families may use *Student Math Handbook* pages 47, 48 and G19–G20 for reference and review. See pages 176–181 in the back of this unit.

Writing Story Problems

Math Focus Points

◆ Understanding division as the splitting of a quantity into equal groups

◆ Writing and solving multiplication problems in context

◆ Writing and solving division problems in context

◆ Using and understanding multiplication notation

◆ Using and understanding division notation

Today's Plan		Materials
ACTIVITY **①** Introducing The Class Multiplication/Division Book	20 MIN CLASS PAIRS	
ACTIVITY **②** Writing Problems for the Class Book	40 MIN INDIVIDUALS	• M14 (as needed)* • Students' multiples charts (from Investigation 2; as needed); cubes (as needed); Array Cards (as needed); unlined paper
SESSION FOLLOW-UP **③** Daily Practice and Homework		• *Student Activity Book,* p. 45 • M34–M35*; Multiplication Cards (as needed) • *Student Math Handbook,* pp. 39, 40–41, 47, 48; G19–G20

*See *Materials to Prepare,* p. 113.

Ten-Minute Math

What Time Is It? What Time will it Be? Show 11:50 on the demonstration clock.
What time is it on this clock? If I start practicing my violin at 11:50 and I practice for 25 minutes, what time will it be when I finish?

In pairs, students share ideas about what time they think it will be. As a class, make sure that students can "cross over" the hour. Focus on counting 25 by 5s. Some students may use the hour as a landmark, breaking 25 into 10 + 15. Ask students a similar question using 8:55 as the starting time and 45 minutes for duration.

Differentiation

① English Language Learners If English Language Learners have trouble writing these story problems, encourage them to begin by drawing sketches of multiplication and division situations. Then you or their classmates can help them put their problems into words. You may want to work with a small group of English Language Learners to edit their writing before they complete their final drafts for the class book.

ACTIVITY

20 MIN   CLASS   PAIRS

1 Introducing the Class Multiplication/Division Book

Explain that over the next few days, each student will write two related story problems—one that is about a division situation, and one that is about a multiplication situation.① All of the problems will then be put together into a Class Multiplication/Division Book.

Write the following expressions on the board:

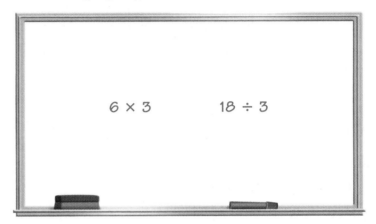

6×3 $18 \div 3$

To get ready for making our class book of problems, we'll work together to make up story problems for 6×3 and $18 \div 3$. Work with a partner to come up with a story problem for each of these two expressions.

After a few minutes, call the class back together. Elicit two problems for each expression. Listen for student understanding of the difference between multiplication and division. For example, do the problems students make for the expression $18 \div 3$ begin with the quantity 18 and divide it into 3 equal groups or groups of 3? Do the problems for 6×3 involve 6 groups of 3 or 3 groups of 6?

ACTIVITY

40 MIN   INDIVIDUALS

2 Writing Problems for the Class Book

For the remainder of the session, students write and solve problems for the class book.

Write a story and draw a picture for it on the front of your paper. On the back of your paper, solve the problem and write the answer. Use the list of "Things That Come in Groups" for ideas. Use any numbers you like. Use cubes, 100 charts, graph paper, or drawings to help you. When you finish one problem, start the next one. Remember to write one multiplication story and one division story.

Students' papers should be similar to the ones below.

Sample Student Work

Sample Student Work

ONGOING ASSESSMENT: Observing Students at Work

Students write multiplication and division story problems.

- **Can students write a story problem that represents division?** Can they write one for multiplication?

- **Are students able to explain their solution?**

DIFFERENTIATION: Supporting the Range of Learners

Intervention Help students talk through the elements of a multiplication situation (two known factors and an unknown product) and a division situation (product and one known factor). Write multiplication and division equations with small numbers and ask students to model the action of each with cubes.

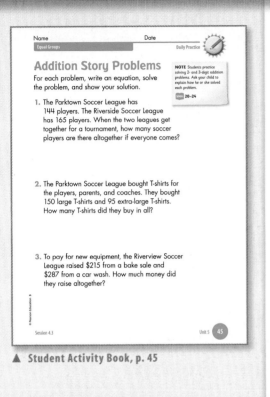

▲ **Student Activity Book, p. 45**

Look at this equation, $3 \times 4 =$ _____ (or $12 \div 4 =$ _____). Can you show me with cubes what this problem would look like? Can you think of a situation to write about in which you might have 3 groups of 4 things (or 12 things divided into groups of 4 or 4 groups)? How can the class posters of "Things That Come in Groups" help you?

Extension Encourage students who are working quickly and easily to use such numbers as 8, 9, 12, or 15.

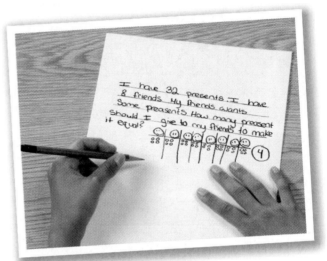

A student uses more challenging numbers to write and illustrate a division problem.

Collect all of the completed stories and bind them together into a Class Multiplication/Division Book.

SESSION FOLLOW-UP
3 Daily Practice and Homework

 Daily Practice: For ongoing review, have students complete *Student Activity Book* page 45.

 Homework: Students continue to practice with their Multiplication Cards for homework, using the directions they have at home. Send home additional copies of the directions *Practicing with Multiplication Cards* (M34–M35) as needed. Also, send home students' Multiplication Cards if they do not have a home set.

 Student Math Handbook: Students and families may use *Student Math Handbook* pages 39, 40–41, 47, 48 and G19–G20 for reference and review. See pages 176–181 in the back of this unit.

Missing Factors

Math Focus Points

◆ Using multiplication combinations to solve division problems

◆ Using the inverse relationship between multiplication and division to solve problems

◆ Using and understanding multiplication notation

◆ Using and understanding division notation

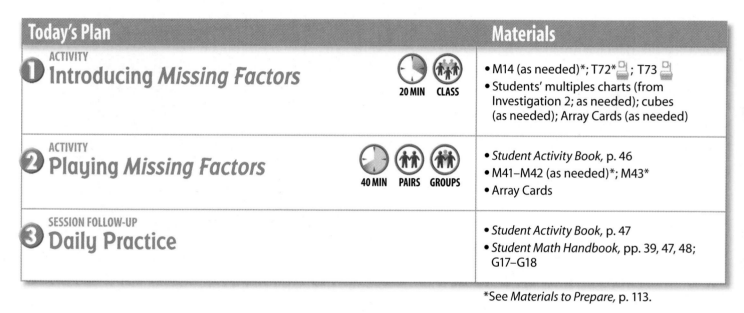

Today's Plan	Materials
ACTIVITY **①** **Introducing** *Missing Factors* 20 MIN CLASS	• M14 (as needed)*; T72*; T73 • Students' multiples charts (from Investigation 2; as needed); cubes (as needed); Array Cards (as needed)
ACTIVITY **②** **Playing** *Missing Factors* 40 MIN PAIRS GROUPS	• *Student Activity Book,* p. 46 • M41–M42 (as needed)*; M43* • Array Cards
SESSION FOLLOW-UP **③** **Daily Practice**	• *Student Activity Book,* p. 47 • *Student Math Handbook,* pp. 39, 47, 48; G17–G18

*See *Materials to Prepare,* p. 113.

Ten-Minute Math

What Time Is It? What Time will it Be? Show 7:40 on the demonstration clock.

What time is it on the clock? If I start my homework at 7:40 and I work for 35 minutes, what time will it be when I finish?

In pairs, student share ideas about what time they think it will be. As a class, make sure students can "cross over" the hour. Focus on counting 35 by 5s. Ask students a similar question using 2:25 as the starting time and 45 minutes for duration.

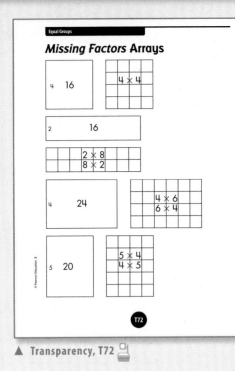

▲ Transparency, T72

ACTIVITY

① Introducing *Missing Factors*

20 MIN CLASS

Introduce *Missing Factors* by showing the product side of the 4 × 6 transparency array (cut from *Missing Factors* Arrays (T72)) on the overhead.

Today I'm going to show you a new array game. In this game, you place your Array Cards in front of you with the product side facing up. What is the information that you know about the array by looking at this card?

Students learn to play Missing Factors.

Students should recognize that the known information is the number of squares in the array (in this case, 24) and one of the dimensions (in this case the number of rows in the array, which is 4).

We know the number of squares and the number of rows in this array. Work with a partner to find the other dimension of the array, which we call the missing factor.

Give students a few minutes to work individually or with a partner to find the missing factor, using any counting tools they like to help them. Before you display the dimension side of the array, have two or three volunteers share their answers and explain how they approached the problem. Strategies may include the following:

- Drawing or building the array step-by-step, adding one row or column of four at a time and keeping track of the number of groups of 4

- Using skip counting charts to find how many 4s are in 24

- Using a related factor pair such as 4×3 to help find the missing factor; for example, $4 \times 3 = 12$, so $4 \times 6 = 24$, making 6 the missing factor

We knew the number of squares in this array and had to divide it into four rows to figure out how many squares were in each row. What is an equation that we can write to represent this problem?

Students should suggest that the problem can be represented with $4 \times \underline{\hspace{1cm}} = 24$ or $\underline{\hspace{1cm}} \times 4 = 24$. Ask what the missing factor would be in each equation. If students do not also suggest the division equation $24 \div 4 = \underline{\hspace{1cm}}$, ask them for it.

Now display the transparency of the *Missing Factors* Recording Sheet (T73) and demonstrate where the equation(s) should be written. Then repeat the entire procedure with at least one more transparency array from *Missing Factors* Arrays (T72).

Finally, go over the game rules together. Emphasize that if the answer they give is not correct, they must return the Array Card to the set with the dimensions side up. At the end of the game they will take turns figuring out the total number of squares on these arrays.

You can use *Missing Factors* (M41–M42) to make extra copies of the rules.

ACTIVITY

2 Playing *Missing Factors*

40 MIN   PAIRS   GROUPS

Students play *Missing Factors* in pairs or small groups. For each array they choose, they record an equation on their recording sheet and circle the missing factor.

If you think that some students have played enough for one day, have them return to their multiplication and division stories for the class book. Encourage them to finish the ones they started or write new ones.

ONGOING ASSESSMENT: Observing Students at Work

Students determine the missing dimension of an array (one factor) when the number of squares in the array and one dimension (the other factor) are given.

- **How do students find the missing factor?** Do they use known multiplication facts? Do they find the missing factor by skip counting or repeated addition?

▲ Resource Masters, M41–M42

▲ Student Activity Book, p. 46
Resource Masters, M43; T73

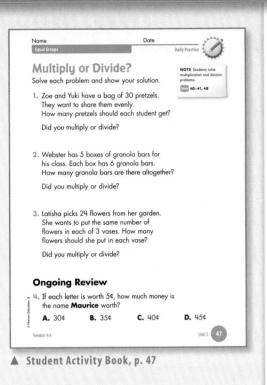

Name _____ Date _____

Equal Groups   Daily Practice

Multiply or Divide?
Solve each problem and show your solution.

NOTE Students solve multiplication and division problems.
[SMH] 40–41, 48

1. Zoe and Yuki have a bag of 30 pretzels.
   They want to share them evenly.
   How many pretzels should each student get?

   Did you multiply or divide?

2. Webster has 5 boxes of granola bars for
   his class. Each box has 6 granola bars.
   How many granola bars are there altogether?

   Did you multiply or divide?

3. Latisha picks 24 flowers from her garden.
   She wants to put the same number of
   flowers in each of 3 vases. How many
   flowers should she put in each vase?

   Did you multiply or divide?

Ongoing Review

4. If each letter is worth 5¢, how much money is
   the name **Maurice** worth?

   A. 30¢   **B.** 35¢   **C.** 40¢   **D.** 45¢

Session 4.4   Unit 5   47

▲ **Student Activity Book, p. 47**

- **Are students able to write multiplication equations that represent the problem accurately?** Are they able to write division equations, understanding that the number of squares in the array are divided into rows or columns by the known dimension?

DIFFERENTIATION: Supporting the Range of Learners

Intervention Questioning students as they work can encourage them to develop more efficient strategies, given the knowledge they have of multiplication relationships. Consider, for example, the Array Card with a product of 28 and a factor of 4.

- Is this one you just know or are you figuring it out?

- How can you figure out how many rows of 4 are in an array of 28?

- Is there a 4s combination (such as 5×4) that will get you partway there?

SESSION FOLLOW-UP

3 Daily Practice

 Daily Practice: For reinforcement of this unit's content, have students complete *Student Activity Book* page 47.

 Student Math Handbook: Students and families may use *Student Math Handbook* pages 39, 47, 48 and G17–G18 for reference and review. See pages 176–181 in the back of this unit.

Solving Multiplication and Division Problems

Math Focus Points

◆ Using multiplication combinations to solve division problems

◆ Using the inverse relationship between multiplication and division to solve problems

◆ Using and understanding multiplication notation

◆ Using and understanding division notation

◆ Identifying and learning multiplication combinations not yet known

Today's Plan		Materials
DISCUSSION **① Different Ways to Write Problems**	20 MIN CLASS	
MATH WORKSHOP **② Practicing Multiplication and Division** **②A** Playing *Missing Factors* **②B** Solving Class Problems **②C** *Practicing with Multiplication Cards*	40 MIN	**②A** • Materials from Session 4.4, p. 129 **②B** • M14 (as needed)* • Materials from Session 4.3, p. 125 • Class Multiplication/Division Books*; students' multiples charts; cubes; Array Cards (as needed) **②C** • M14 (as needed)*; M27*; M34–M35* • Students' multiples charts; cubes; Array Cards (as needed); Multiplication Cards
SESSION FOLLOW-UP **③ Daily Practice**		• *Student Activity Book,* p. 48 • *Student Math Handbook,* pp. 39, 40–41, 47, 48, 49–51; G17–G18, G19–G20

*See *Materials to Prepare,* p. 113.

Ten-Minute Math

What Time Is It? Show 2:15 on the demonstration clock. Ask students:

• What time is it on the clock? If I left my house one day at 2:15 and returned at 3:30, how long was I gone?

In pairs, students share ideas about what they think. Ask students a similar question using 8:10 as the starting time and 9:15 as the ending time.

DISCUSSION

1 Different Ways to Write Problems

Math Focus Points for Discussion

◆ Using and understanding multiplication notation

◆ Using and understanding division notation

Begin the session by asking students to relate multiplication and division notation to story problems. Tell students that you will say a story problem and they will give examples of notation for it. Explain that you are not asking them to solve the problem at this time.

Six friends collected bottles and cans to bring to the redemption center. The cashier gave them $24 for all of the bottles and cans. The friends shared the money equally. How much money did each friend receive?

How could I notate this with numbers? Is there any other way?

Provide a few more examples for students, mixing up multiplication and division story problems. Then switch and give students an example of notation and ask them to make a story problem to match it. Write notations such as the following on the board:

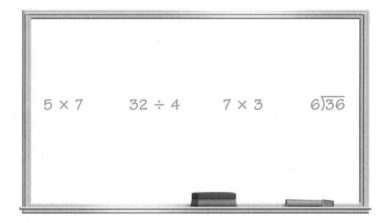

$$5 \times 7 \qquad 32 \div 4 \qquad 7 \times 3 \qquad 6\overline{)36}$$

2 Practicing Multiplication and Division

40 MIN

Students work on the activities listed below during the remainder of this session and most of the next session. Make sure that all students spend time on each activity. Tell students that cubes, Array Cards, 100 charts, and other tools are available for their use for each activity.

2A Playing *Missing Factors*

PAIRS

For complete details about this activity, see Session 4.4, page 130.

2B Solving Class Problems

INDIVIDUALS PAIRS

Tell students to choose one problem from the class book of multiplication and division problems and solve it on a separate sheet of paper. They should write the problem at the top of the paper and their solution underneath. Tell students to show how they solved the problem, being sure to include the equation that represents their work.

Students work alone or with a partner to solve a problem written by a classmate.

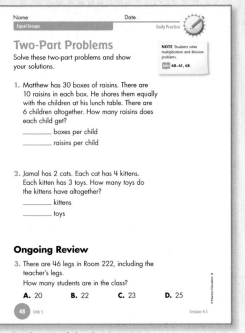

▲ Student Activity Book, p. 48

ONGOING ASSESSMENT: Observing Students at Work

Students solve multiplication and division problems written by their classmates.

- **Can students accurately solve both multiplication and division problems?**

- **Are students able to explain their solutions?** Do they include the proper use of notation?

DIFFERENTIATION: Supporting the Range of Learners

Intervention Suggest to students having trouble writing division sentences to first write a multiplication sentence with a question mark or a blank to represent the missing information. Model for them how to write the related division equation.

2C *Practicing with Multiplication Cards*

INDIVIDUALS

For complete details about this activity, see Session 3.5, pages 103–105.

SESSION FOLLOW-UP
3 Daily Practice

Daily Practice: For reinforcement of this unit's content, have students complete *Student Activity Book* page 48.

Student Math Handbook: Students and families may use *Student Math Handbook* pages 39, 40–41, 47, 48, 49–51 and G17–G18, G19–G20 for reference and review. See pages 176–181 in the back of this unit.

Solving Multiplication and Division Problems, *continued*

Math Focus Points

◆ Using multiplication combinations to solve division problems

◆ Using the inverse relationship between multiplication and division to solve problems

◆ Using and understanding multiplication notation

◆ Using and understanding division notation

◆ Identifying and learning multiplication combinations not yet known

Today's Plan		Materials
MATH WORKSHOP ❶ **Practicing Multiplication and Division,** *continued* ⓐ Playing *Missing Factors* ⓑ Solving Class Problems ⓒ *Practicing with Multiplication Cards* ⓓ Playing *Count and Compare*	🕐 **40 MIN**	ⓐ • Materials from Session 4.4, p. 129 ⓑ • Materials from Session 4.5, p. 133 ⓒ • Materials from Session 3.5, p. 101 ⓓ • Materials from Session 3.6, p. 107
DISCUSSION ❷ **Solving Division Problems**	🕐 👪 **20 MIN CLASS**	
SESSION FOLLOW-UP ❸ **Daily Practice**		• *Student Activity Book,* p. 49 • *Student Math Handbook,* pp. 39, 40–41, 47, 48, 49–51; G9, G17–G18, G19–G20

*See *Materials to Prepare,* p. 115.

Ten-Minute Math

What Time Is It? Write 11:33 on the board, and have students show it on their clocks.

How did you know to show the time on the clock?

Can you say the time aloud?

Do you know that the time can also be read as 33 minutes past 11:00?

How many minutes is it before 12:00?

Ask additional similar questions using times that are in between five-minute intervals, such as 7:43, 6:22, and 9:09.

40 MIN

MATH WORKSHOP

1 Practicing Multiplication and Division, *continued*

Students continue with these Math Workshop activities from Session 4.5.

1A Playing *Missing Factors*

PAIRS

For complete details about this activity, see Session 4.4, page 130.

1B Solving Class Problems

INDIVIDUALS PAIRS

For complete details about this activity, see Session 4.5, page 135. Remind students to write the problem at the top of the page and their solution with an explanation underneath. Students' work should be similar to the following:

> A chocolate chip cookie has 5 chocolate chips in it. If there are 6 chocolate chip cookies, how many chocolate chips are there?
>
> I know that 5 x 5 = 25 because its square so one more 5 is 30 chocolate chips

Sample Student Work

there were 15 eggs on each of
the shelves there were 6 shelves
How many eggs altogether?

Sample Student Work

1C Practicing with Multiplication Cards

INDIVIDUALS

For complete details about this activity, see Session 3.5, pages 103–105.

1D Playing *Count and Compare*

PAIRS **GROUPS**

This game is for students who you feel have spent enough time on the first three activities in the Math Workshop. For complete details about this activity, see Session 3.6, page 108.

DISCUSSION

20 MIN **CLASS**

2 Solving Division Problems

Math Focus Points for Discussion

◆ Using multiplication combinations to solve division problems

◆ Using the inverse relationship between multiplication and division to solve problems

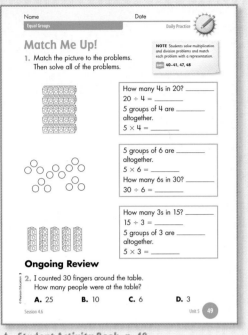

▲ Student Activity Book, p. 49

Choose two or three division problems from the class book and ask students to share their strategies for solving each one. Record strategies as students share, and focus the discussion on strategies in which students used multiplication combinations they knew to find the answer to the division problem.

For example, ask the questions below about the following problem: I have 32 markers. I will make packs of markers and put eight markers in each pack. How many full packs of markers can I make?

How did you start solving this division problem? Is there a multiplication combination you know that might help you? What part of the problem have you solved? What is left to solve?

Students might say:

"I knew that two packs of markers would have 16 markers. One more pack would use up 24 of the markers. And one more would use all 32."

"I started with 8 and skip counted up until I got to 32. I skip counted four times, so I know that I can make four packs."

Remind students that they will continue to practice their multiplication combinations throughout the rest of the year and that these combinations can be very helpful in solving division problems. If each student has a class book of multiplication and division problems, they can continue to solve problems at home.

SESSION FOLLOW-UP

3 Daily Practice

Daily Practice: For reinforcement of this unit's content, have students complete *Student Activity Book* page 49.

Student Math Handbook: Students and families may use *Student Math Handbook* pages 39, 40–41, 47, 48, 49–51 and G9, G17–G18, G19–G20 for reference and review. See pages 176–181 in the back of this unit.

End-of-Unit Assessment

Math Focus Points

◆ Understanding multiplication as combining equal groups

◆ Understanding division as the splitting of a quantity into equal groups

◆ Understanding the relationship among skip counting, repeated addition, and multiplication

◆ Using and understanding multiplication notation

◆ Using and understanding division notation

Today's Plan		Materials
ASSESSMENT ACTIVITY ① **End-of-Unit Assessment**	✓ 🕐 👤 60 MIN INDIVIDUALS	• M14 (as needed)*; M44* • Students' multiples charts (from Investigation 2; as needed); cubes (as needed); Array Cards (as needed)
SESSION FOLLOW-UP ② **Daily Practice**		• *Student Activity Book,* p. 50 • *Student Math Handbook,* pp. 39, 40–41, 47, 48, 49–51

*See *Materials to Prepare,* p. 115.

Ten-Minute Math

What Time Is It? Write 6:49 on the board and ask students to show it on their clocks.

How did you know to show the time on the clock?

Can you say the time aloud?

Do you know that the time can also be read as 11 minutes before 7:00?

Ask additional similar questions using times that are in between five-minute intervals, such as 7:07, 10:27, and 9:12.

Professional Development

❶ **Teacher Note:** Assessment: End-of-Unit Assessment, p. 165

Name _____ Date _____

Equal Groups

End-of-Unit Assessment

Solve the problems and show your solutions.
Write equations that represent the problems.

Problem 1

Insects have 6 legs.

A. How many legs are on 3 insects?

B. How many legs are on 6 insects?

Problem 2

Keisha's father baked 36 muffins for the third-grade bake sale. Keisha put the muffins in bags. She put 4 muffins in each bag. How many bags of muffins did she have for the bake sale?

© Pearson Education 3

M44 Unit 5   Session 4.7

▲ **Resource Masters, M44** PORTFOLIO

ASSESSMENT ACTIVITY

❶ End-of-Unit Assessment

60 MIN   INDIVIDUALS

Provide students with copies of the End-of-Unit Assessment (M44). Students solve problems that assess their understanding of multiplication and division as involving groups of equal groups.❶ These problems assess the following benchmarks for the unit.

Benchmark 1: Demonstrate an understanding of multiplication and division as involving groups of equal groups.

Benchmark 2: Solve multiplication combinations and related division problems by using skip counting or known multiplication combinations.

Benchmark 3: Interpret and use multiplication and division notation.

As students work, remind them to write an equation for each problem after they have solved it. If some students use multiplication notation for a problem, ask them to also write the division notation. When students complete the assessment, they may return to the math workshop activities of previous sessions.

The goal of this assessment is for most students to be able to solve the problems, show their solutions, and write equations to represent the problems.

ONGOING ASSESSMENT: Observing Students at Work

Students use their knowledge of multiplication and division to solve the problems on the assessment.

- **Do students' solutions demonstrate an understanding of multiplication and division as involving equal-size groups?**

- **Are students able to solve these problems by using strategies involving skip counting or known combinations, or do they need to model the action of the problems by using cubes, drawings, or other methods?**

- **Do students use known multiplication combinations to determine the products of more difficult combinations?**

- **Are students able to correctly write multiplication and division equations?**

DIFFERENTIATION: Supporting the Range of Learners

Intervention Some students may have answers to the problems but may be having trouble writing their strategies. Have these students explain their thinking to you and record it for them on their paper. Note that these students need ongoing support in recording their strategies for themselves.

SESSION FOLLOW-UP

2 Daily Practice

Daily Practice: For enrichment, have students complete *Student Activity Book* page 50.

Student Math Handbook: Students and families may use *Student Math Handbook* pages 39, 40–41, 47, 48, 49–51 for reference and review. See pages 176–181 in the back of this unit.

Name   Date

Equal Groups   Daily Practice

Smart Savings

How much money could you save in 1 year? What could you buy with that money?

NOTE Students multiply several numbers by 12.

If I save this much each month . . .	I will save this much in a year!	This is what I could buy at the end of 1 year.
1. $1		
2. $2		
3. $3		
4. $4		
5. $5		
6. $6		
7. $7		
8. $8		

50   Unit 5   Session 4.7

▲ **Student Activity Book, p. 50**

Equal Groups

In Part 6 of *Implementing Investigations in Grade 3,* you will find a set of Teacher Notes that addresses topics and issues applicable to the curriculum as a whole rather than to specific curriculum units. They include the following:

Computational Fluency and Place Value

Computational Algorithms and Methods

Representations and Contexts for Mathematical Work

Foundations of Algebra in the Elementary Grades

Discussing Mathematical Ideas

Racial and Linguistic Diversity in the Classroom:
    What Does Equity Mean in Today's Math Classroom?

Teacher Note

Images of Multiplication

It is important that students develop strong visual images of multiplication as they develop strategies for solving multiplication problems. If students can visualize clearly how the numbers they are multiplying are related, they can develop flexible, efficient, and accurate strategies for solving multiplication problems.

Students encounter many ways to represent multiplication in Grade 3—pictures of groups of things in a story context, skip counting on a 100 chart, and arrays. As students work with larger numbers in Grades 3 and 4, it will become cumbersome to draw pictures, skip count on a large number chart, or use arrays with all the individual units shown. Students need to learn to visualize these representations mentally to help them break up the numbers and keep track of which parts of the problem have been solved and which remain to be solved.

As you work with students, suggest these ways of visualizing multiplication, especially when a student cannot figure out where to start or when a student has solved part of a problem and is unsure how to continue.

Images of Equal Groups in a Story Context

In this unit students learn to represent a multiplication expression such as 6×4 by creating a picture similar to this one:

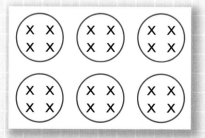

Ask students to generate simple stories that help them visualize a multiplication expression such as 6×4 as equal groups; for example, six bags with four marbles in each bag. Help students select contexts that are familiar to them. Then you can ask students to imagine that context as a way of thinking through the problem. In Grade 3, students are moving away from thinking of multiplication as repeated addition. Instead of adding up 4s, students can be encouraged to use the image to start with a larger chunk of the problem. For example, you might ask, "Can you visualize how many marbles would be in two bags? In three bags? Now how many more bags of four are there?" A story context involving equal groups can help students use what they know to determine the product: "I know that there are 12 marbles in three of the bags, and there are three more bags, so I double that to get 24."

Representing Multiplication as Skip Counting

In this unit, students mark off multiples of the numbers 2–6 and 10 on 100 charts.

1	2	3	4	5	6	7	8	9	10
11	12	13	14	15	16	17	18	19	20
21	22	23	24	25	26	27	28	29	30
31	32	33	34	35	36	37	38	39	40
41	42	43	44	45	46	47	48	49	50
51	52	53	54	55	56	57	58	59	60
61	62	63	64	65	66	67	68	69	70
71	72	73	74	75	76	77	78	79	80
81	82	83	84	85	86	87	88	89	90
91	92	93	94	95	96	97	98	99	100

Hundreds chart with multiples of 3 shaded.

These charts provide an opportunity for students to notice patterns in each number's multiples and to consider the relationship between multiples of various numbers (for example, all of the multiples of 4 also show up on the multiples of 2 chart). Ask students questions that help them visualize the counting number sequence and think through how to calculate the next multiple as they are skip counting. For example, "You said that you've counted by 8s to 48. What is a way of quickly figuring out what 8 more will be?" If students use skip counting to solve a less familiar multiplication combination, encourage them to start with a known multiple and then continue to skip count. For example, to solve 3×12, students may know that $3 \times 10 = 30$ and then make two more jumps in their mind, to 33 and then 36.

Representing Multiplication with Arrays

In this unit, students work with Array Cards and drawings in which all the individual units of the array are visible. These rectangular arrays are a representation of groups and amounts in a group in any multiplication problem.

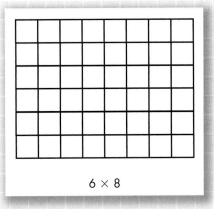

6×8

This 6×8 array can be seen as 6 groups of 8 items or 8 groups of 6 items. In either case, students can visualize the problem as a whole and the smaller parts that may help them to find the product; for example, if juice boxes come in sets of 6, a student might think of 8×6 as 8 sets of juice boxes. The student could visualize these in an array and use that image to break the problem into parts that are easier to solve.

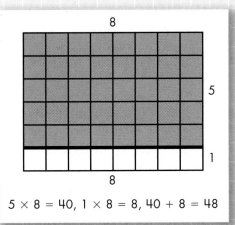

$5 \times 8 = 40, 1 \times 8 = 8, 40 + 8 = 48$

Visualizing how to break multiplication problems into parts becomes even more important as students solve multidigit problems in Grades 4 and 5. See the **Teacher Note:** Representing Multiplication with Arrays (page 157), for more information about how arrays are used in this unit and how the use of arrays can be extended to represent more difficult multiplication and division problems.

Teacher Note

Representing Multiplication with the Number Line

In earlier Grade 3 units, students used the number line to show addition and subtraction. In this unit, students use the number line to show that multiplication involves equal groups. Students see that skip counting on the number line is a useful addition to skip counting on the 100 chart. Although it does not show the patterns in relationship to 10 that are visible on the 100 chart, skip counting on the number line clearly shows the accumulation of equal groups.

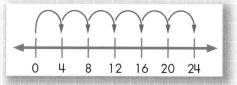

This representation may be particularly useful when students are working with doubling and halving in Investigation 2. For example, as students consider the relationship between multiples of 5 and 10 or multiples of 3 and 6, some students may use the number line to justify their arguments.

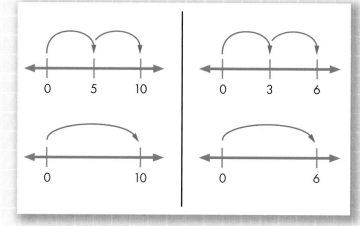

See Kathryn's reasoning in **Dialogue Box:** Relationships Between the Multiples of 5 and 10 (page 170).

Teacher Note

The Relationship Between Multiplication and Division

Multiplication and division are related operations. For example, here is a set of linked multiplication and division equations:

$$8 \times 9 = 72 \qquad 72 \div 9 = 8$$

$$9 \times 8 = 72 \qquad 72 \div 8 = 9$$

The multiplication equations show the multiplication of two factors to equal a product. The division equations show the product (dividend) divided by one of the factors (divisor) to equal the other factor (quotient). Some problem situations your students encounter in this unit can be described as both multiplication and division.

Consider the following problem:

I have a supply of 48 treats for my dog. If I give her 6 treats every week, how many weeks will the supply last?

The quantities in this problem are 48 treats, 6 treats per week, and a number of weeks to be determined. This problem can be written in standard notation as either multiplication or division.

$$48 \div 6 = \underline{\hphantom{xx}} \text{ or } \underline{\hphantom{xx}} \times 6 = 48$$

After the answer to the problem has been found, both division and multiplication equations can be written to show the relationship of the three quantities.

48 treats divided into groups of six (six treats per week) results in eight groups (weeks).

$$48 \div 6 = 8$$

8 weeks with 6 treats per week equals 48 treats.

$$8 \times 6 = 48$$

When students solve a problem like this one, they may write either a division or multiplication equation to express the answer and its relationship to the quantities in the problem. Both notations represent the problem, depending on whether the student is thinking of the problem as division or as a multiplication problem with a missing factor. They should be able to read and interpret both of these notations, explaining what each number in the equation represents, and relating the equation to the original problem.

See **Algebra Connections in This Unit** (page 16) for more about understanding the inverse relationship between division and multiplication.

Assessment: Solving Problems About Our Pictures

Students choose items to illustrate from the class lists of "Things That Come in Groups." They write sentences describing the number of groups, the number in each group, and the product and write multiplication equations for their illustrations.

Benchmarks addressed:

Benchmark 1: Demonstrate an understanding of multiplication and division as involving groups of equal groups.

Benchmark 3: Interpret and use multiplication and division notation.

Note: In this assessment, students are assessed on multiplication; they are assessed on division in the End-of-Unit Assessment.

In order to meet the benchmarks, students' work should show that they can:

- Illustrate a multiplication situation that shows a number of equal-size groups;

- Identify the number of groups, the number in each group, and the product in this situation;

- Write a multiplication equation to represent the problem.

Note that students are not being assessed on their solution strategies at this point in the unit; however, you can also use this task to begin identifying what support students are likely to need as the unit continues. See the last section of this Teacher Note for suggestions.

Meeting the Benchmark

The following examples of student work provide a range of typical responses. All of these students meet the benchmarks—they were able to clearly describe the parts of their multiplication situation in words and with an equation.

Philip illustrated three sets of baseball cards with seven cards in each set. He wrote three sentences correctly describing the number of groups, the number in each group, and the product and wrote a multiplication equation that accurately represented this multiplication situation.

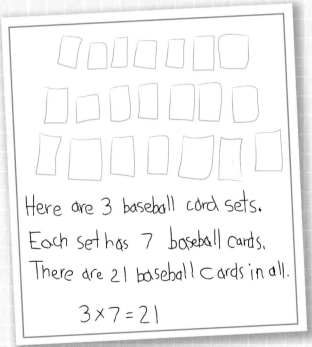

Here are 3 baseball card sets.
Each set has 7 baseball cards.
There are 21 baseball cards in all.

$3 \times 7 = 21$

Philip's Work

Deondra drew five pairs of shoes and wrote three sentences correctly describing the number of groups, the number in each group, and the product. She wrote a multiplication equation that accurately represented this multiplication situation.

Here are 5 pairs of shoes.
Each pair has 2 shoes.
There are 10 shoes in all
$$5 \times 2 = 10$$

Deondra's Work

Partially Meeting the Benchmarks

Adam drew six hexagons and wrote three sentences correctly describing the number of groups, the number in each group, and the product. He did not, however, write a multiplication equation to represent his illustration.

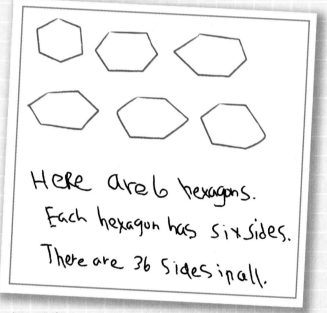

Here are 6 hexagons.
Each hexagon has six sides.
There are 36 sides in all.

Adam's Work

To determine whether a student like Adam understands how to use multiplication notation to represent a problem or whether he simply forgot that part of the assessment, ask him what equation he could write.

Gina drew five cans of tennis balls with three balls in each can. She correctly wrote three sentences describing the number of groups, the number in each group, and the product. However, rather than writing a multiplication equation, she wrote the addition equation $3 + 3 + 3 + 3 + 3 = 15$.

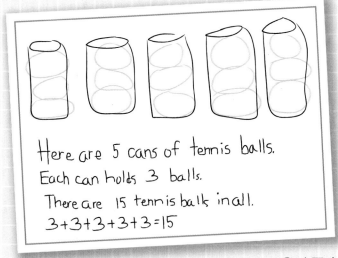

Gina's Work

Ask questions to determine whether students like Gina know the multiplication equation that represents $3 + 3 + 3 + 3 + 3 = 15$. "What kind of equation did you write? How many groups of 3 are in your picture? How would you write this as multiplication?"

Not Meeting the Benchmarks

These students do not show equal size groups. A student may draw two groups of unequal size, such as one bag of 6 apples and a second bag of 4 apples, and add to find the sum.

Looking at students' approaches to finding the product

Although we are not assessing student approaches to solving these problems at this point in the unit, this assessment does provide the opportunity to look at how students determine the products in their multiplication situations. Expect a range of strategies, including drawing the groups and counting by ones, skip counting by the number in each group, repeated addition, and starting with a known multiplication combination.

Help those students counting by ones think about more efficient ways to find the product. Ask them what groups they see in their pictures that they could count by instead.

Help students who are skip counting by asking questions such as the following to help them connect what they are doing to multiplication notation: "How many times did you skip count (by 4s) to find the product? How many groups (of 4) is that? Can you write that in a multiplication equation? Do you know how much 2 groups (of 4) would be? Can you use an easier combination (such as 2×4) to help you find the answer (to 6×4)?"

Students are assessed on their ability to solve multiplication problems in Sessions 2.5 and 2.6.

Patterns in the Skip-Counting Charts

In Investigation 2, students create a set of 100 charts on which they highlight the multiples of 2, 3, 4, 5, 6, and 10. Students enjoy creating these charts and, as they do so, they are becoming familiar with the multiples of these numbers. Their work with these charts also focuses on relationships between multiples of pairs of numbers in which one number is twice the other. See **Dialogue Boxes:** Relationships Between the Multiples of 5 and 10 (page 170) and Bags of 6, Bags of 3 (page 171).

Students will also notice the different patterns of numbers on the different charts. For example, the highlighted multiples on the 2s, 5s, and 10s charts are in columns, and the highlighted multiples on the 3s chart form a diagonal pattern. The 4s and 6s have their own distinct patterns as well.

Students will continue these patterns visually but are not necessarily thinking about why these patterns occur. These patterns arise because of relationships between numbers and their factors. In the paragraphs that follow, a question about these patterns is posed. Some mathematical information is provided about the pattern, along with suggestions for questions you may ask students. You may want to work on each question yourself before reading the explanation. Keep in mind that third graders will not necessarily be ready to engage with all of these questions. However, some students may find them intriguing and may go further with them.

Why do some sets of multiples fall in columns but others do not?

The multiples of 2, 5, and 10 fall in straight columns on the 100 chart. The numbers 2, 5, and 10 are all factors of 10. For example, because 2 is a factor of 10, each row of 10 squares can be divided evenly into 2s. The multiples fall on every second square, ending on 10. This pattern repeats in every row because there is the same number of groups of 2 in each row of 10.

The number 3 is not a factor of 10, that is, it does not evenly divide 10. The multiples of 3 fall on every third square, so the last square they fall on in the first row is the ninth square. To get to the next multiple, we must count the "leftover" square in the first row and 2 more squares in the second row. Because we need only 2 squares in the second row to complete this group of 3, the multiples in the second row are shifted by 1 square to the left. By the end of the second row, 2 squares are left, and again the squares in the third row are shifted 1 to the left. Because three rows of 10 contains groups of 3 with no leftovers, our skip counting lands on the last square in the third row, the thirtieth square. Because counting in the fourth row now begins from the first square, the pattern that occurred in the first, second, and third rows now repeats.

Questions to ask students: Why do the multiples of 5 fall in straight columns on the 100 chart? Why are there two columns on the 100 chart for the multiples of 5? (Ask similar questions for 2s and 10s.) Why don't the multiples of 3 make straight columns on the 100 chart? Can you predict when you will highlight a multiple of 3 in the column under 10? Why does this happen?

Challenge questions: Cut off the last column on a blank 100 chart, so that there are nine squares in each row. Number the squares from 1–9 in the first row, 10–18 in the second row, and so on up to 90. Ask students to highlight multiples of 2 on one chart and multiples of 3 on another chart. Now the 2s do not fall in columns, but the 3s do. Why does this occur? Try other sets of multiples. Try another size chart. What happens on a chart with six in a row, seven in a row, eight in a row, 12 in a row?

Compare numbers that are highlighted on the 2s and 6s charts or on the 3s and 6s charts. What can you say about these numbers?

All of the multiples of 6 are both multiples of 2 and multiples of 3. Because both two and three are factors of six, any multiple of 6 is also a multiple of 2 and of 3. Another way to look at this is that three groups of 2 is 6, so every three jumps of 2 on the 100 chart is a jump of 6 squares. The first three jumps of 2 land on 6, the next three jumps get to 12, and so on. Every three jumps of two reaches the next multiple of 6. Similarly, two jumps on the 3s chart gets to the next multiple of 6. Therefore, every number on the 6s chart appears on both the 2s chart and the 3s chart. Unlike the previous question about patterns in columns, this relationship is not dependent on the number of squares in the rows of a counting chart. No matter how the counting chart is set up (rows of nine, for example), the multiples of 6 will always appear on both the 2s and 3s charts. These relationships among the numbers hold, no matter the shape of the chart.

Questions to ask students: Find the numbers that are on the 2s chart and the 6s chart. What can you say about these numbers? Do you notice any pattern? Can you describe a rule to find the numbers that will be on both charts? Can you predict the next five numbers that will be on both charts? (You can ask the same questions for any pair of charts for which one number is a factor of the other, such as 2s and 4s or 2s and 8s.)

Compare numbers that are highlighted on both the 2s and 3s charts. What can you say about these numbers?

Comparing these two charts leads to different observations than for the 2s and 6s or 3s and 6s. Some of the numbers on the two charts are the same, but not all of them. The numbers that are the same fall on every third number highlighted on the 2s chart and every second number highlighted on the 3s chart, as in this chart, on which the multiples of 2 are circled and the multiples of 3 have Xs through the square:

Because 6 is the smallest number with factors of both 2 and 3 (the least common multiple of 2 and 3), the only numbers common to the two sets of multiples are, in fact, the multiples of 6. Every six squares on the 100 chart contains groups of 2 squares with no leftovers and groups of 3 squares with no leftovers. Like the relationship in the previous question, this relationship is not affected by the number of squares in rows of the counting chart.

Questions to ask students: Find the numbers that are highlighted on both the 2s and 3s charts. Do you notice any pattern? How can you describe which numbers are on both charts? Can you describe a rule to find the numbers that will be on both charts? Can you predict the next five numbers that will be on both charts?

Students' Problems with Skip Counting

Some students have difficulty keeping track of their skip counting on the 100 chart. Here are some confusions we have noticed in the classrooms:

- Some students always start on 1, no matter which number they are skip counting by.

- The count may get off by 1 because the student pauses at a circled number and then starts counting again with that number. For example, when counting by 6s, a student counts 6, 12, 18 and then begins the next count on 18. After counting six more numbers (18, 19, 20, 21, 22, 23), the student lands on 23 instead of 24.

- Students sometimes follow a "false pattern" that does not actually work for the number they are counting by. For example, they may circle 3, 6, and 9, then color straight down the columns under the 3, 6, and 9, not realizing that the 3s pattern does not continue in columns the way the 2s pattern does.

- Students may miscount one interval and then continue counting correctly, so all subsequent numbers are affected by the original mistake. For example: 3, 6, 9, 12, 15, 19, 22, 25, 28 . . .

Some of these difficulties are simply miscounting mistakes that anyone can make. Help students use the pattern on their counting charts to check: Does the pattern continue consistently on the chart? Also, have students double-check one another. When two or three students compare charts, they can often find and correct their own miscounting.

However, some students may truly not understand what they are doing when they "count by 2s" or "count by 3s" on their charts. Here, using cubes as a first step will help. When counting by 2s, the student makes a group of 2 cubes and then marks 2 on the chart; makes another group of 2 cubes (perhaps in a different color) and marks the total, 4; then makes another group of cubes, marks the total, 6; and so on. Students will naturally stop using the cubes as soon as they feel comfortable with skip counting.

We have found that it is not helpful for students to use cubes to mark squares directly on the counting charts. Students cannot see the numbers underneath them, and they often move a cube accidentally to a neighboring square, thereby misleading themselves about the pattern on the chart.

Assessment: *Counting Around the Class*

Benchmark addressed:

Benchmark 2: Solve multiplication combinations and related division problems by using skip counting or known multiplication combinations.

In order to meet the benchmark, students' work should show that they can:

- Skip count accurately by 3; or

- Use a known multiple of 3 (e.g., $3 \times 3 = 9$, $3 \times 4 = 12$, $3 \times 10 = 30$) to find the product of 3×9 or 3×11.

At this point in the unit, students should be using strategies based on making groups, rather than counting by ones, to solve multiplication problems.

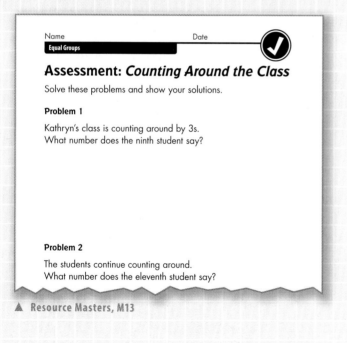

▲ Resource Masters, M13

Meeting the Benchmark

The following examples of student work provide a range of typical responses. All of these students meet the benchmark —they solved the problems by skip counting or by using known combinations. They also used the solution to 9×3, or another known combination such as 10×3 or 5×3, to solve 11×3.

Becky solved Problem 1 by skip counting. She accurately counted groups of three up to 27. She found how many multiples of 3 she had by first identifying the fifth multiple (15) and then counting how many more 3s she had.

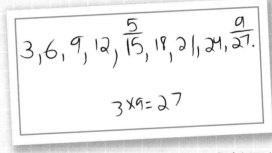

Becky's Work

Elena began Problem 1 with a known multiplication combination, 4×3. She was able to keep track of how many groups of three she had (working her way up to 27). She doubled the product of 4×3 and then added one more 3.

I Know that 4×3=12 and 12+12=24 which would be 8 3's 24+3=27 and that's 9 3's

Elena's Work

Students may also use other combinations. For example, they may start with 5×3, double it, and subtract one group of three.

For Problem 2, Deondra used what she knew from solving Problem 1.

> It will be 33 because it is two more groups of 3 than 27.   27+6= 33

Deondra's Work

Partially Meeting the Benchmark

Some students may have a solid understanding of the connection between skip counting and the meaning of multiplication as groups but may have incorrectly skip counted.

Zhang has missed the multiple 18 in his skip counting sequence and so incorrectly counts 10 groups of three.

> I know the times because if you count 10 numbers down all you have to do is 3x10=
> 3 6 9 12 15 21 24 27 30 33
> 33

Zhang's Work

When students' work shows incorrect computation, ask whether they have checked it. In Zhang's case, looking back at the equation he has written, $3 \times 10 = 33$, may also help him see his mistake, because many students are familiar with multiples of 10. If not, ask him to go back and look at his Multiples of 10 chart to see what he notices about all of the highlighted numbers. Students who skip count inaccurately may also revisit their multiples charts and match the sequences they generated to the highlighted numbers on their charts.

Not Meeting the Benchmark

Some students may be relying on physical models such as cubes and 100 charts to solve the problems. These students still need to construct the problem precisely and count either each cube or each number on the 100 chart individually, as Bridget does.

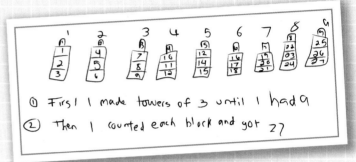

① First I made towers of 3 until I had 9
② Then I counted each block and got 27

Bridget's Work

Students such as Bridget may get an accurate answer, but the focus for them during the rest of the unit should be on learning to use groups rather than counting by ones. Ask students like Bridget whether there is anything about groups of three they already know that might help them. ("How many are in two groups of three? How many are in three groups of three? Can you use what you know to help you find how many are in four groups? Six groups?")

These students also need opportunities to practice skip counting, either during *Counting Around the Class* or by filling out more skip counting charts. They can also benefit from working on more related problem sets, such as those on *Student Activity Book* pages 14–16.

Representing Multiplication with Arrays

Representing mathematical relationships is a key element of developing mathematical understanding. In Grade 3, students first encounter multiplication as "groups of" as they brainstorm lists of things that come in equal groups of various sizes and create multiplication situations from those lists. These contexts help them develop visual representations which give meaning to multiplication expressions. For example, 5 × 4 can be visualized as 5 dogs with 4 legs each or 5 rectangles with 4 sides on each rectangle.

Students extend their understanding of multiplication through their work with arrays. For multiplication, the rectangular array is an important tool. It meets all the criteria for a powerful mathematical representation: it highlights important relationships, provides a tool for solving problems, and can be extended as students apply ideas about multiplication in new areas.

Why Arrays for Multiplication?

Students use rectangular arrays to represent the relationship between a number and its factors: the area of the array is the number, and the length and width of the rectangle are one pair of factors of that number (e.g., a 3 × 4 rectangle with an area of 12).

As students come to understand the operation of multiplication in Grades 3 and 4, they gradually move away from thinking of multiplication only as repeated addition. They learn that multiplication has particular properties that distinguish it from addition. Although a number line or 100 chart can show how multiplication can be viewed as adding equal groups, neither of these tools provides easy access to other important properties of multiplication. The rectangular array provides a window into properties that are central to students' work in learning the multiplication combinations and in solving multidigit multiplication and division problems.

For example, suppose that students are working on one of the more difficult multiplication combinations, 6 × 8. They might think of splitting this multiplication in this way: 6 × 8 = (3 × 8) + (3 × 8). In doing so, they are using the distributive property of multiplication, which can be represented by using an array.

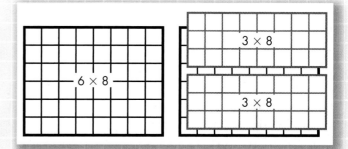

Each number that you break up into parts must be multiplied by the other number. The array shows how one dimension of the rectangle (6) is split into parts (3 + 3) to form two new rectangles, each with the dimensions 3 × 8. This property of multiplication is at the core of almost all common strategies used to solve multiplication problems.

The rectangular array also makes it clearer why the product of 6 × 8 is the same as the product of 8 × 6. The array can be rotated to show that six rows with eight in each row has the same number of squares as eight rows with six in each row. The column on one becomes the row on the other, illustrating the commutative property—the fact that you can change the order of two factors in a multiplication expression without changing the product.

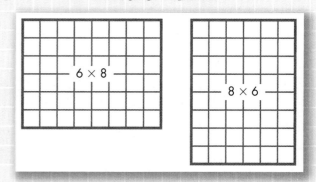

Arrays in this unit serve as a powerful tool for helping students learn multiplication combinations. At first, students often count by the number in a row or column of an array (for example, counting by 8 six times or 6 eight times for the array pictured on page 157). Gradually, they learn to use arrays to visualize how to use known combinations to solve those they are working on ($3 \times 8 = 24$, therefore 6×8 equals twice that amount or 48).

Arrays also support students' learning about the relationship between multiplication and division. In a division problem such as $48 \div 6$, the dividend (48) is represented by the number of squares in the array, and the divisor (6) is one dimension of the array. Students develop strategies for division as they find the missing dimension of arrays like the one below.

Students can think of "slicing off" pieces of the rectangle as they gradually figure out the other factor.

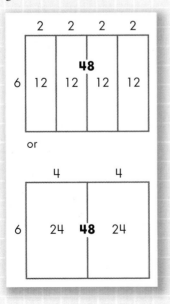

In later grades, arrays are particularly useful for solving or visualizing how to solve multidigit multiplication problems. After students have worked with rectangular arrays for single-digit multiplication combinations and thoroughly understand how an array represents the factors and product, they can use arrays in work later in Grade 4 to solve harder problems. The array for 28×25 can be broken up in many ways.

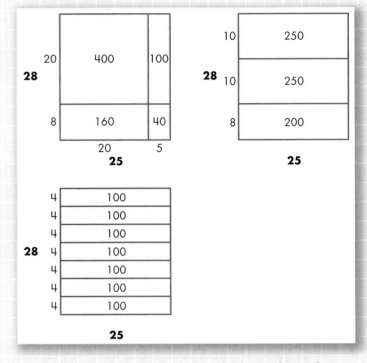

Each of these ways suggests an approach to solving this problem.

Finally, the use of the rectangular array can be extended in later grades as students work with multiplication of fractions and, later, of algebraic expressions.

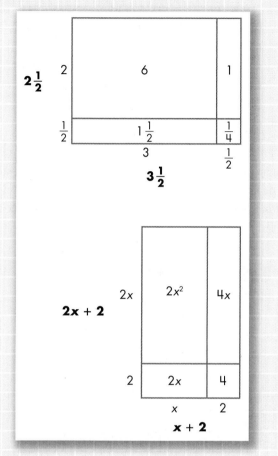

Labeling Arrays

For multiplication notation to describe arrays, the *Investigations* curriculum uses the convention of designating the number of rows first and the number in each row second; for example, 3 × 2 indicates three rows with two in each row.

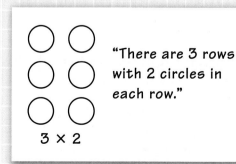

This convention is consistent with using 3 × 2 to indicate 3 groups of 2 in other multiplication situations (e.g., 3 pots with 2 flowers in each pot). However, it is not necessary or useful to spend time getting students to follow this system rigidly; trying to remember which number stands for rows and which for the number in a row can be unnecessarily distracting for students. When students suggest a multiplication expression for an array, what is important is that they understand what the numbers mean; for example, a student might show how 3 × 2 represents 3 rows of cans with 2 in each row or 3 cans in each of 2 rows.

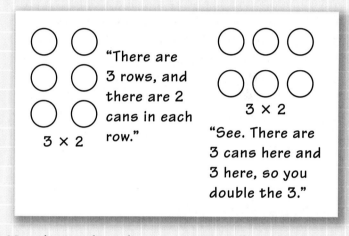

Note that in other cultures, conventions about interpreting multiplication expressions differ. In some countries, the convention for interpreting 3 × 2 is not "3 groups of 2" but "3 taken 2 times."

Learning Multiplication Combinations

Students are expected to learn the multiplication combinations with products up to 50 by the end of Grade 3 and will be assessed on these combinations during Unit 8, *How Many Hundreds? How Many Miles?* They are expected to know the combinations through 12 × 12 by the end of Grade 4.

Students will work on the multiplication combinations throughout this unit, but many will need additional practice after this unit is completed. You can use the Multiplication Cards for this purpose. With your guidance about which multiplication combinations to work on, students should continue learning these combinations at home or outside of math time. You may have other favorite practice methods or activities that you want to suggest for particular students. Also, enlist parents or other family members in helping with practice. This Teacher Note provides recommendations for supporting students in this ongoing practice.

Why Do We Call Them Combinations?

The pairs of factors from 1 × 1 through 12 × 12 are traditionally referred to as "multiplication facts"—those multiplication combinations with which students are expected to be fluent. The *Investigations* curriculum follows the National Council of Teachers of Mathematics (NCTM) convention of calling these expressions *combinations* rather than *facts*. *Investigations* does this for two reasons. First, naming only particular addition and multiplication combinations as facts seems to give them elevated status, more important than other critical parts of mathematics. In addition, the term *fact* implies that something cannot be learned through reasoning. For example, it is a fact that the first president of the United States was George Washington, and it is a fact that Rosa Parks was born in Alabama in 1913. If these facts are important for us to know, we can remember them or use reference materials to look them up. However, the product for the multiplication combination 6 × 7 can be determined in many ways; it is logically connected to our system of numbers and operations. If we

forget the product but understand what multiplication is and know some related multiplication combinations, we can find the product through reasoning. For example, if we know that 5 × 7 = 35, we can add one more 7 to determine that the product of 6 × 7 is 42. If we know that 3 × 7 = 21, we can reason that the product of 6 × 7 would be twice that, 2 × (3 × 7) = 42.

The term *facts* does convey a meaning that is generally understood by some students and family members, so you will need to decide whether to use the term *facts* along with *combinations* in certain settings in order to make your meaning clear.

Learning the Multiplication Combinations Fluently

Like NCTM, this curriculum supports the importance of students' learning the basic combinations fluently through a focus on reasoning about number relationships: "Fluency with whole-number computation depends, in large part, on fluency with basic number combinations— the single digit addition and multiplication pairs and their counterparts for subtraction and division. Fluency with basic number combinations develops from well-understood meanings for the four operations and from a focus on thinking strategies." Principles and Standards for School Mathematics, (2000) pages 152–153.

Fluency means that combinations are quickly accessible mentally, either because they are immediately known or because the calculation that is used is so effortless as to be essentially automatic (in the way that some adults quickly derive one combination from another).

Helping Students Learn the Multiplication Combinations with Products up to 50

For many students starting out in Grade 3, learning multiplication combinations may seem overwhelming— an endless mass of combinations with no order and reason. Therefore, bringing order and reason to students' learning of multiplication combinations in a way that lets them have control over their progress is essential. Traditionally, students learned one "table" at a time—first the ×2 combinations, then the ×3 combinations, the ×4 combinations, and so on. However, the multiplication combinations can be grouped in other ways to support learning related combinations.

First, make sure that students know all multiplication combinations that involve ×0, ×1, ×2, ×5, and ×10 (up to 10 × 10) fluently. (Note that, although most third graders can easily count by 2, 5, and 10, the student who is fluent does not need to skip count to determine the product of multiplication combinations involving these numbers.) Knowing that multiplication is commutative is crucial for learning all the multiplication combinations. The work with Array Cards supports this understanding (see **Teacher Note:** Representing Multiplication with Arrays, page 157). When these combinations are known, provide students with a sequence of small groups of the multiplication combinations they still need to review that they can relate to what they already know. There are a number of ways to do this. Here is a three-step method we recommend:

1. Learning the ×4 combinations

Work on the ×4 combinations that students do not yet know: 3 × 4, 4 × 4, 6 × 4, 7 × 4, 8 × 4, and 9 × 4 (and 4 × 3, 4 × 6, and so on). Help students think of these as doubling the ×2 combinations—4 × 6 = (2 × 6) + (2 × 6) or 4 × 6 = 2 × (2 × 6). Students may verbalize this idea as "4 times 6 is 2 times 6 and another 2 times 6," or "to get 4 times 6, I double 2 × 6." Doubling is also useful within the ×4 combinations; for example, when students know that 3 × 4 = 12, then that fact can be used to solve 6 × 4: 6 × 4 = (3 × 4) + (3 × 4). Getting used to thinking about doubling with smaller numbers will also prepare students for using this approach with some of the harder combinations.

2. Learning the square numbers

Students learn or review the three remaining combinations that produce square numbers less than 50: 3 × 3, 6 × 6, and 7 × 7. These are often easy for students to remember. If needed, use doubling or a known fact for "start with" clues during practice (e.g., 6 × 6 is double 3 × 6; 7 × 7 = (4 × 7) + (3 × 7). Students can also build these with tiles or draw them on squared paper to see how they can be represented by squares.

3. Learning the remaining facts with products up to 50

Learn or review the six remaining facts with products up to 50: 3 × 6 through 3 × 9, 7 × 6, and 8 × 6. First relate them to known facts (e.g., double 3 × 3 or halve 6 × 6 to get 3 × 6) and then practice them.

Our benchmark is for third graders to learn the combinations up to 50, but some third graders will go beyond that benchmark. For example, most will learn the ×10 combinations through 100, and many will use the patterns of the ×11 and ×12 combinations to learn these through 100 as well. Some students may be ready and eager to learn more.

Students Who Know Their Combinations up to 50

Although this is not the focus in Grade 3, students who know their combinations up to 50 and the combinations that involve multiplying by 10 up to 100 (6 × 10, 7 × 10, 8 × 10, 9 × 10, 10 × 10) can work on learning the more difficult combinations. Here is one way of sequencing this work:

1. Learning the remaining combinations with products up to 100

There are six difficult combinations to learn (other than the ×11 and ×12 combinations, which are, in fact, not as difficult as these and are discussed below). These six difficult combinations are 6 × 9 (and 9 × 6), 7 × 8 (and 8 × 7), 7 × 9 (and 9 × 7), 8 × 8, 8 × 9 (and 9 × 8), and 9 × 9.

Students can work on one or two of these most difficult multiplication combinations each week. Make sure that they use combinations they do know to help them learn those they do not know—for example, $8 \times 7 = 2 \times (4 \times 7)$ or $9 \times 7 = (10 \times 7) - 7$. They can write these related multiplication combinations as "start with" hints on the Multiplication Cards. If most of your class needs to work on the same few hard combinations, you may want to have the whole class focus on two of these each week.

2. Learning the ×11 and ×12 combinations

We consider these combinations to be in a different category. Historically, these combinations were included in the list of "multiplication facts." However, when we are dealing with 2-digit numbers in multiplication, an efficient way to solve them is through applying the distributive property; i.e., breaking the numbers apart by place as you would with any other 2-digit numbers. However, we include them here because some local or state frameworks still require knowing multiplication combinations through 12×12. In addition, 12 is a number that occurs often in our culture, and it is useful to know the ×12 combinations fluently. Most students learn the ×11 combinations easily because of the pattern 11, 22, 33, 44, 55, . . . created by multiplying successive whole numbers by 11. They should also think through why this pattern occurs: $3 \times 11 = (3 \times 10) + (3 \times 1) = 30 + 3 = 33$. They should think through why $11 \times 10 = 110$ and $11 \times 11 = 121$ by breaking up the numbers. Students can learn the ×12 combinations by breaking the 12 into 10 and 2, e.g., $12 \times 6 = (10 \times 6) + (2 \times 6)$. Some students may also want to use doubling or adding on to known combinations: $12 \times 6 = 2 \times (6 \times 6)$ or $12 \times 6 = (11 \times 6) + 6$.

Fluency Benchmarks for Learning Facts Through the Grades

- **Addition** End of Grade 2; review and practice in Grade 3

- **Subtraction** End of Grade 3; review and practice in Grade 4

- **Multiplication** Multiplication combinations with products up to 50 by the end of Grade 3; up to 12×12 by the end of Grade 4

- **Division** End of Grade 5

Two Kinds of Division: Sharing and Grouping

In this unit, students encounter two kinds of division situations. Consider these two problems:

I have 18 balloons for my party. After the party, I'm going to divide them evenly between my sister and me. How many balloons will each of us get?

I have 18 balloons for my party. I'm going to tie them together in bunches of two to give to my friends. How many bunches can I make?

Each problem is a division situation—a quantity is broken up into equal groups. The problem and the solution for each situation can be written in standard notation as $18 \div 2 = 9$. Yet these two situations are actually quite different. In the first situation, the *number of groups* of balloons (2) is given. The question is "How many balloons will be in each group?" In the second situation, the number of balloons *in each group* (2) is given, and the question is "How many groups will there be?" Each problem involves equal groups of balloons, but the results of the actions look different.

I have 18 balloons and two people. How many balloons does each person get?

I have 18 balloons to put into bunches of two. How many bunches will there be?

The solution to each problem is 9, but in the first problem 9 is the number of balloons per person (the number in each group). In the second problem, 9 is the number of bunches of balloons (the number of groups).

The first situation is probably the one with which your students are most comfortable because it can be solved by "dealing out;" that is, the action to solve the problem might be: one for you, one for me, one for you, one for me until all the balloons are given out. In this situation, division is used to describe *sharing*. A more formal term for this kind of problem is *partitive* division—a division situation in which something is distributed, and the problem is to determine *how many are in each group*.

In the second situation, the action to solve the problem is making groups—that is, making a group of two, then another group of two, and another, and so on until no balloons are left. In this situation, division is used to describe *grouping*. This situation is sometimes called "measurement division" because the total amount is measured out into equal groups. The formal term for this kind of division situation is *quotative* division—a situation in which *how many equal groups* must be determined.

By working with a variety of problems in this unit, students learn to recognize both of these actions as division situations and to develop an understanding that both can be written in the same way: $18 \div 2 = 9$. Depending on the context, help students interpret the notation as either "Divide 18 into two groups. How many are in each group?" or "How many 2s are in 18?"

As students become more flexible with division, they will understand that they can solve a sharing problem by thinking of it as grouping or a grouping problem by thinking of it as sharing in order to make it easier to solve.

How many people are on each team if I make 25 equal teams from 100 people?

To solve this problem, it is easy to think, "How many groups of 25 are in 100?" even though the problem is not about groups of 25, but about 25 groups. The numerical answer to this grouping question is also the numerical answer to the sharing problem. Some of your students may soon have an intuitive understanding that they can solve a division problem by thinking about it either way. Students can draw on what they know about multiplication, that 4 teams of 25 is the same number of people as 25 teams of 4 ($4 \times 25 = 25 \times 4$). This understanding is based on the commutative property of multiplication (See **Algebra Connections in This Unit,** page 16.).

End-of-Unit Assessment

Problem 1

Benchmarks addressed:

Benchmark 1: Demonstrate an understanding of multiplication and division as involving groups of equal groups.

Benchmark 2: Solve multiplication combinations and related division problems by using skip counting or known multiplication combinations.

Benchmark 3: Interpret and use multiplication and division notation.

In order to meet the benchmarks, students' work should show that they can:

- Interpret the story problem as being about 3 groups of 6 legs and then 6 groups of 6 legs;

- Accurately multiply 3 × 6 and 6 × 6 by either skip counting or using a known combination;

- Write correct multiplication equations.

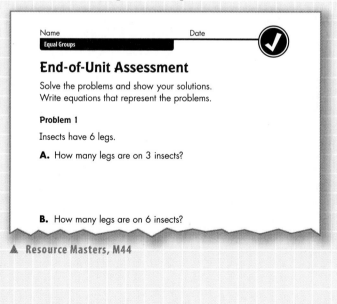

Name _____ Date _____
Equal Groups

End-of-Unit Assessment

Solve the problems and show your solutions.
Write equations that represent the problems.

Problem 1

Insects have 6 legs.

A. How many legs are on 3 insects?

B. How many legs are on 6 insects?

▲ **Resource Masters, M44**

Meeting the Benchmarks

The following examples of student work provide a range of typical responses. All of these students met the benchmarks—they were able to interpret, solve, and notate the problem correctly.

Denzel found the answer to both parts of the problem by skip counting. He represented the groups of 6 legs in the problem and wrote multiplication equations.

$$6, 12, \boxed{18} \qquad 3 \times 6 = 18$$
$$6, 12, 18, 24, 30 \ \ 36 \qquad 6 \times 6 = 36$$
$$\ \ 1 \ \ 2 \ \ 3 \ \ 4 \ \ 5 \ \ \ \ 6$$

Denzel's Work

Kim's work shows that she interpreted the problem correctly as being about groups of 6. For the first part of the problem, she added one more group of 6 to 6 × 2 (presumably a known combination). For the second part of the problem, she showed that there are twice as many groups of 6 and doubled the result of 3 × 6 to find the product of 6 × 6.

$$6 \times 2 = 12 \qquad 12 + 6 = 18$$
$$6 \times 3 = 18 \ legs$$
$$18 + 18 = 36$$
$$6 \times 6 = 36 \ legs$$

Kim's Work

Gina also used a combination she knows, 3 × 3, to find the product of 3 × 6.

$$3 \times 3 = 9 \qquad 9 + 9 = \boxed{18} \quad \text{legs on } 3$$
$$18 \times 2 = 36 \searrow \text{ legs on } 6$$

Gina's Work

Adam wrote that he just "knew" 6 × 3 and 6 × 6. There is no evidence of counting or representing in Adam's work.

I knew that 3×6 = 18 and 6×6 = 36

Adam's Work

Pilar represented the groups of insect legs with a picture and then wrote the correct equations. It is unclear how she found the products; there is no evidence of counting or adding. It may be that Pilar, like Adam, "just knows" these combinations and therefore meets the benchmarks.

18 legs   3 × 6 = 18

6 × 6 = 36

Pilar's Work

Observing students like Adam and Pilar as they work and questioning them about their thinking would provide more evidence about whether they have met the benchmarks. Pilar and Adam's teacher probably knows from their previous work in the unit whether they "just know" these combinations. If, for example, she knew that Pilar was just making the transition from counting by ones to counting by groups, she would make a point of observing Pilar or asking her about her solution.

Partially Meeting the Benchmarks

These students may have a solid understanding of multiplication as groups but may have incorrectly skip counted, written incorrect equations, or not used multiplication notation.

Benjamin demonstrated a strong understanding of the groups of 6 and accurately combined these groups, but he did not use multiplication notation.

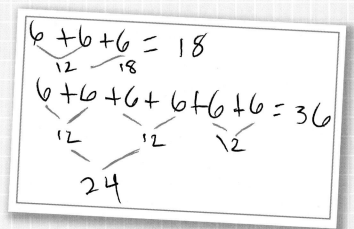

$$6 + 6 + 6 = 18$$
$$\quad 12 \quad 18$$
$$6 + 6 + 6 + 6 + 6 + 6 = 36$$
$$\quad 12 \quad \quad 12 \quad \quad 12$$
$$24$$

Benjamin's Work

Kelley interpreted the problem as "three 6s" and solved the problem by adding one more 6 to two 6s but then wrote an incorrect equation.

$$6 + 6 = 12 \qquad 12 + 6 = 18$$
$$6 \times 2 = 18$$

Kelley's Work

When students' work shows incorrect computation or leaves out part of the problem, ask whether they have gone back to check their work. Students like Kelley, who are unclear about how to use multiplication notation, may need to have this modeled for them. Use the skip counting circles on the Multiples Charts to help these students identify which numbers in the problem represent the number of groups, the number in each group, and the product.

Not Meeting the Benchmarks

A few students may still be unclear about the meaning of situations involving equal groups and may not interpret the problems correctly.

Arthur did not consider each insect as a group of 6 legs and seemed to be answering the question "How many legs does an insect have?" by adding some number to the given information.

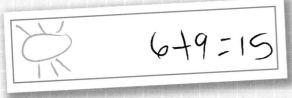

Arthur's Work

Ines represented each of the three insects with a drawing, but she did not respond to the multiplication question "How many legs are on 3 insects?"

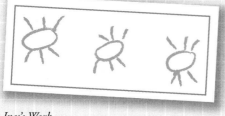

Ines's Work

Students like Arthur and Ines need to do more work on representing multiplication situations with cubes, drawings, and skip counting tools.

Problem 2

Benchmarks addressed:

Benchmark 1: Demonstrate an understanding of multiplication and division as involving groups of equal groups.

Benchmark 2: Solve multiplication combinations and related division problems by using skip counting or known multiplication combinations.

Benchmark 3: Interpret and use multiplication and division notation.

In order to meet the benchmarks, students' work should show that they can:

- Interpret the story problem as "how many groups of 4 are there in 36?";

- Determine the number of bags of muffins by either skip counting or using a known combination;

- Write a division equation.

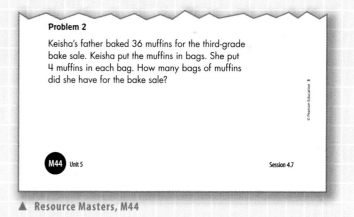

Problem 2

Keisha's father baked 36 muffins for the third-grade bake sale. Keisha put the muffins in bags. She put 4 muffins in each bag. How many bags of muffins did she have for the bake sale?

M44   Unit 5   Session 4.7

© Pearson Education 3

▲ **Resource Masters, M44**

Meeting the Benchmarks

The following examples of student work provide a range of typical responses. All of these students met the benchmarks—they were able to interpret, solve, and notate the problem correctly.

Nancy interpreted the problem as a division situation, skip counted to find how many 4s are in 36, and wrote a division equation.

Nancy's Work

Kathryn accurately represented the problem with a drawing and wrote a division equation.

Kathryn's Work

Keith used multiplication combinations he knew to find the answer to the division problem. Students like Keith recognize that they are solving the related problem $4 \times \underline{\hspace{1cm}} = 36$.

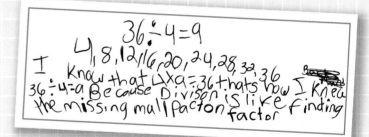

Keith's Work

Nicholas used knowledge of the inverse relationship between multiplication and division. He knew the multiplication combination 4×9 and recognized the inverse as $36 \div 4 = 9$.

Nicholas's Work

Partially Meeting the Benchmarks

Some students may attempt to solve the division problem by finding the number of equal groups but may incorrectly skip count or multiply. Students who solve these problems by repeated addition or subtraction demonstrate an understanding of the structure of the problem, but at this point in the year, they should be using skip counting or known combinations.

Beatriz clearly and accurately represented the problem as involving equal groups but did not use either multiplication or division notation.

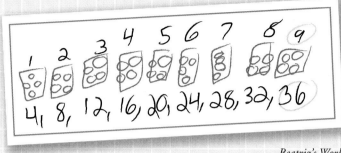

Beatriz's Work

Jane accurately skip counted but wrote the division equation incorrectly.

$$4, 8, 12, 16, 20, 24, 28, 32, 36$$

$$9 \div 4 = 36$$

Jane's Work

Edwin used only repeated addition, adding one more 4 each time until he reached 36.

$$4 + 4 + 4 + 4 + 4 + 4 + 4 + 4 + 4 = 36$$

Edwin's Work

When students' work shows incorrect computation or leaves out part of the problem, ask whether they have gone back to check their work. Students who are not using notation correctly may need to have it modeled for them. Students who are relying on repeated addition should be encouraged to use small multiplication combinations, such as 4×2, and build from there rather than adding one group at a time.

Not Meeting the Benchmarks

These students may not yet be making sense of division situations. They may be able to represent the situation concretely with cubes or drawings but may not understand what they are trying to find.

Cristobal did not understand that he was supposed to find the number of groups.

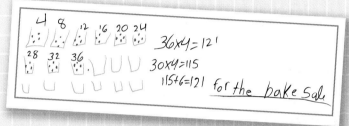

Cristobal's Work

Bridget divided the 36 muffins into 4 bags, but she did not make equal groups.

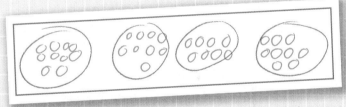

Bridget's Work

Students like Cristobal and Bridget need to do more work representing division situations with cubes and drawings, with an emphasis on making equal groups and identifying the different parts of the problem (how many in each group, number of groups, and total amount).

Relationships Between the Multiples of 5 and 10

After highlighting the multiples of 5 and 10 on separate 100 charts, students are discussing the patterns they notice.

Teacher: You noticed that every other multiple of 5 is a multiple of 10, and that there are twice as many multiples of 5 as multiples of 10. Why do you think this is true?

Becky: 5 is half of 10.

Gil: There are two 5s in 10, so you just double it.

Teacher: What do you mean by "just double it"?

Gil: You take this, [holds up a tower of 10] and if you break it in half, [he does] you have 2 towers of 5. So for a multiple of 5, you double what you have with 10.

Teacher: Gil showed us that 1 tower of 10 can be broken into 2 towers of 5. Can that help us figure out how many groups of 5 are in 20?

Gil: There are two 10s in 20 and two 5s in each 10, so there are 4 groups of 5 in 20. [Gil breaks 2 towers of 10 in half and counts out loud.] "1, 2, 3, 4."

Becky: It can also mean that because 10 is twice as big as 5, I only need half as many 10s as 5s. So let's say I know that there are 4 fives in 20—then I know that there are only two 10s in 20. If you already know how many 5s you have, you double that to find out how many 10s you have! Can I show you with Gil's towers? [Becky snaps the 4 towers of 5 back together to make 2 towers of 10.]

Teacher: Can someone explain this in a different way?

Kathryn: On the number line it takes 2 jumps of 10 to get to 20, but it takes 4 jumps of 5 to get to 20. You land at the same place, but it's more jumps with 5s. It's because inside every jump of 10, there are 2 jumps of 5. 4 is double the 2.

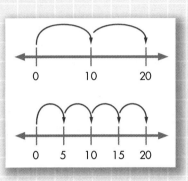

Teacher: How do Kathryn's number lines show that there are twice as many multiples of 5 on the 100 chart as there are multiples of 10? Who can explain it?

Kim: You can keep going to 30, 40, 50, up to 100. Every time you make 1 jump for the 10s, you make 2 jumps for the 5s.

Keith: You can even keep going farther, to 200 or 300. No matter how far you go, it's always 2 for 1. The 5 jumps are always double the 10 jumps.

Teacher: Can anyone give us a story context that we could use to show this? What is something we could have in groups of 5 or groups of 10?

Kenji: You could have plates with 5 or 10 crackers.

Teacher: Let's say that every square on our 100 chart is a cracker. We have 100 crackers. How many plates do we need if we put five crackers on each plate? How many plates do we need if we put ten crackers on each plate?

Students modeled the relationship between the multiples of 5 and 10 in a variety of ways. Making representations helped students both understand and explain this relationship and act out what happened when one of the factors in a multiplication expression was doubled or halved. Students in this class at first chose towers of 10 and number lines to illustrate their ideas. The teacher then asked students to use a context because she knows that different students make sense through different images.

Dialogue Box

Bags of 6, Bags of 3

After working on the problems on *Student Activity Book* pages 19–20, Counting Around by 3s and 6s and Bags of Apples, the teacher brings the class together to discuss what students notice about the relationship between the multiples of 3 and the multiples of 6.

Teacher: I want to look back at the work you did on the story problems about bags of apples and counting around the class. I'm interested to hear from you about how you can use the information that 30 groups of 6 equal 180 to prove that 30 groups of 3 equal 90.

Beatriz: I know that 90 + 90 equals 180. So I know that if 30 bags of 6 apples equal 180 apples, then 30 bags of 3 apples will equal 90.

Teacher: How do you know that?

Beatriz: Because the bags of 6 are twice as big as the bags of 3, so she needs half as many apples for 30 bags of 3.

Teacher: Can someone use their own words to explain what Beatriz is saying?

The teacher waits, but only two students raise their hands.

Teacher: Let's think about this with smaller numbers. Let's say that Ms. Ross wants to fill 5 bags of apples. The first week she fills each bag with 6 apples. How many apples will she need?

Gil: 30.

Teacher: What can I sketch on the board to quickly show 5 bags with 6 apples in each bag?

Adam: You can do it with Xs. Put 6 Xs for one bag, then put another 6 Xs and keep going for every bag.

```
x   x   x   x   x
x   x   x   x   x
x   x   x   x   x
x   x   x   x   x
x   x   x   x   x
x   x   x   x   x
1   2   3   4   5
```

Teacher: Five bags filled with 6 apples in each uses up 30 apples. $5 \times 6 = 30$. The next week she fills 5 new bags with 3 apples. How many apples will she need?

Oscar: 60.

Teacher: Why 60?

Nora: Wouldn't it be 15?

Teacher: What would make it 15?

Becky: $3 \times 5 = 15$.

Teacher: What do you mean by your numbers? What are the 3, 5, and 15 standing for?

Becky: Three bags—no, 5 bags—and you put 3 apples in each one. That's 15 apples.

Teacher: Who can use our picture of 5 bags with 6 apples in each to show what happens the second week? Does she have more apples or fewer apples when each bag has 3 in it compared with when it had 6?

Kenji: Fewer apples.

Teacher: Does she have a certain number fewer? Who can show us, using this picture?

Philip: Half as many. At first she needed 30 apples but now she only needs 15. Can I come up and show you?

Philip draws a horizontal line, splitting each column of Xs in half.

Philip: The bags are only the part below the line now.

```
        x   x   x   x   x
        x   x   x   x   x
        x   x   x   x   x
       ─────────────────────
        x   x   x   x   x
        x   x   x   x   x
        x   x   x   x   x
        1   2   3   4   5
```

Oscar: Can I change my answer? I get it now! You take 3 out of each bag and you only have 3 left. I was mixing up my answers.

Teacher: Let's use different numbers and see whether that connection works again. Let's use 5 and 10.

The teacher quickly sketches 5 columns with 10 Xs in each.

Teacher: Now Ms. Ross puts ten apples in each bag the first week. She still is making 5 bags of apples. How many apples will she need?

Benjamin: 50.

Teacher: The next week she filled each bag with only 5 apples. Without doing any skip counting, how can you figure out how many apples she needs?

Kim: It would be 25.

Teacher: What makes you say 25?

Kim: 25 is half of 50. It's like what Philip did. Every bag is half as full.

At first, few students are participating in this discussion. To give more students access to the problem, the teacher uses smaller numbers and then gets a representation up early in the discussion so that students can work with a visual image of the problem. Although Adam does not suggest a particular configuration for the Xs, the teacher organizes them in a way that will help students see the relationship between 6 apples in a bag and 3 apples in a bag. She then builds on the use of this representation but changes the numbers students are considering so that they begin to reason about what happens in any multiplication situation when one factor is halved. She keeps the discussion grounded in the context of bags and apples so that students do not get lost in the numbers, as Oscar does at first.

Arranging Chairs

Two pairs of students are discussing whether they have found all of the possible rectangular arrangements for 24 chairs. Some students are moving around cubes to find each array, and others are using grid paper to draw rectangles.

Teacher: Let's see all of the arrays you have found for 24. Do you think you have found them all?

Bridget: We found three ways to arrange the chairs: one row of 24, two rows of 12, and four rows of 6. That's three, and I think we are done.

Arthur: Wait, I have another: 6 × 4 (points to cubes arranged in six rows of four cubes each). I don't see this rectangle in your three.

Teacher: What's different about Arthur's arrangement and Bridget's last one?

Ines: There's really nothing different, it's just turned on its side.

Teacher: Can anyone else see what Ines is saying?

Arthur: Now that I look at both of ours, I can see that they are kind of the same. They are exactly the same if you flip mine to be next to hers. You could put one on top of the other.

Teacher: So one has six rows of four, or 6 × 4, and the other has four rows of six, or 4 × 6. You're right—they can be placed directly on top of each other. But if you were setting up chairs to watch a movie, they would be different arrangements, so let's have both on our list. We have 1 × 24, 2 × 12, 6 × 4, and 4 × 6. Do you think there are any other ways we could make equal rows of 24 chairs? How did you find these?

Arthur: I tried different numbers of rows until I found ones that came out even. Actually, 24 × 1 was an easy one. And I knew that 24 was an even number, so I knew that 2 fit in evenly because 2 fits into every even number.

Bridget: I tried 5 and thought it was going to work until I got to the last row and realized that there was one too many. Five would work for 25, but not 24.

Inez: It seems to me that there are more arrangements because 24 is such a big number.

Bridget: I was just playing around and found out that 3 fits into 24 eight times! I didn't try 3 at first because it just didn't seem like it would fit in.

In this discussion, students are sharing several ideas about finding arrays, including that some arrays are exactly the same but are labeled differently and that all even numbers will have an array with one dimension of 2. Although trying out random numbers will allow you to find some of the factors, it is generally not a useful or efficient way to find all of the factors. At this point in students' work, some are trying various numbers and others are beginning to notice some connections among the dimensions of different arrays. As students have more time to work on finding arrays independently, the teacher will help them notice some important relationships among the arrays for related numbers. For example, every factor of 12 will also fit into 24 twice as many times (e.g., 2 × 6 = 12, 2 × 12 = 24). Some students will also organize their work by ordering the dimensions in a sequenced list.

Dialogue Box

Finding the Number of Squares in an Array

After making sets of Array Cards in the previous math session, students are discussing their strategies for finding the number of squares in arrays. The teacher puts the 6 × 6 Array Card on the overhead.

Teacher: What are some ways that we can figure out the number of squares in this array?

Benjamin: You can count every square, but that takes a long time and, like you told us, it's easy to make a mistake that way.

Jung: We can skip count by sixes. 6, 12, 18, 24, 30, 36.

As Jung counts, the teacher records the numbers under each column.

Edwin: I cut it in half. I did three groups of six and got 18 and I knew the bottom part was the same. I added 18 and 18 and got 36.

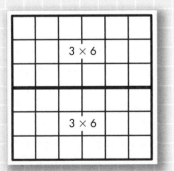

Teacher: So you used a combination that you know, 3 × 6 = 18, to help you figure out the one that you don't know, 6 × 6.

The teacher records (3 × 6) + (3 × 6) = 6 × 6 under the array.

Teacher: Did anyone else use a strategy like Edwin's?

Ines: We saw three groups of 12. We know that two groups of 6 is 12, so we added 12 + 12 + 12.

Adam: We did 12 + 12 = 24, and then 24 + 12 = 36.

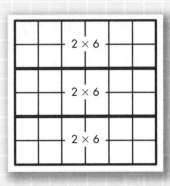

The teacher records 6 × 6 = (2 × 6) + (2 × 6) + (2 × 6) under the array.

Keisha: I used 3 × 3 because I know that that's 9 and then I added the 9s to get 36.

Teacher: Can you show us where you see the 3 × 3 inside the 6 × 6 array?

Keisha goes to the overhead and shows the four 3 × 3 arrays embedded in the 6 × 6 array.

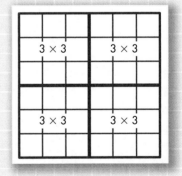

This teacher has encouraged her students to use combinations they know or to count by equal groups to determine the product represented by an array. In discussions, and as students work independently, she asks students to think of ways to begin with a piece of the problem that they know. She wants them to use efficient ways to find the product. She also models how to use mathematical notation to record their strategies. By asking students to explain or demonstrate where they see the smaller arrays within the larger one, she helps all her students visualize how to break a difficult multiplication combination into easier parts.

Is It Multiplication or Division?

After solving Problem 2 on *Student Activity Book* page 42, Story Problems, students are discussing whether it represents a multiplication or a division situation and what operation can be used to solve it. The students are also comparing ways to notate both multiplication and division problems.

Teacher: What information is given in this problem?

Edwin: There are 20 muffins that need to be put into bags. Each bag gets four muffins.

Teacher: And what is the question we are trying to answer?

Jung: How many bags of muffins do we have?

Teacher: In what way is this problem different from Problem 1 that we talked about yesterday? Take a look at Problem 1 on your paper and tell me what information we have and what we are trying to find out.

Keisha: In Problem 1, we don't know the number of fingers.

Teacher: We don't know the total. What *do* we know?

Keisha: The number of hands. Oh, and how many fingers are on each hand.

Teacher: So how are Problem 1 and Problem 2 different? I noticed that some of you used cubes to solve each of these problems. Did you do something different with the cubes?

Denzel: When I solved the one about the muffins, I made groups out of the bigger number. And when I solved the one about the robot, I counted up all the fingers to get how many there were altogether. Do you know what I mean?

Teacher: Can anyone say more about what Denzel explained?

Keisha: The muffin problem is division.

A general mumbling of surprise goes through the room. "We're doing division?" "Are we going to do division now in math?" "Division is really hard!"

Teacher: Why do you think the muffin problem is a division problem?

Denzel: Because I divided the muffins up! I made small groups out of a big number.

Adam: But wait. I multiplied to get my answer to the muffin problem. So it's a multiplication problem.

A few other students say that they also multiplied.

Teacher: Tell us what you multiplied.

Adam: I just knew that $4 \times 5 = 20$. So you'd have five bags of muffins.

Teacher: I can see that some of you are nodding so you must have thought about it the same way. So even though this is a division situation—that is, you know the total and divide the total up to find the number of groups—you can still solve it by using multiplication. How can we write an equation for the muffin problem?

Jung: 20 divided by 4 equals blank.

Teacher: How do you make the "divided by" sign?

Adam: Two dots with a line in the middle. Can I show you on the board?

Adam writes $\div$ on the board.

The teacher then asks students to write an equation for Problem 1 ($4 \times 6 = 24$). In this discussion, the teacher is starting a conversation that will continue throughout Investigation 4. Students continue to think about the difference between multiplication and division situations and how to notate each one.

Student Math Handbook

The *Student Math Handbook* pages related to this unit are pictured on the following pages. This book is designed to be used flexibly: as a resource for students doing classwork, as a book students can take home for reference while doing homework and playing math games with their families, and as a reference for families to better understand the work their children are doing in class.

When students take the *Student Math Handbook* home, they and their families can discuss these pages together to reinforce or enhance students' understanding of the mathematical concepts and games in this unit.

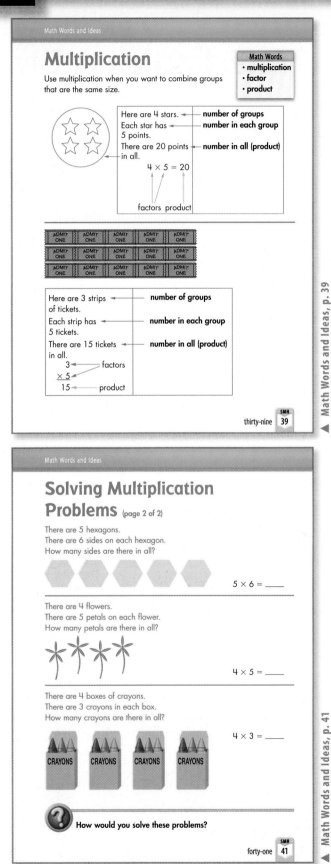

▲ Math Words and Ideas, p. 39

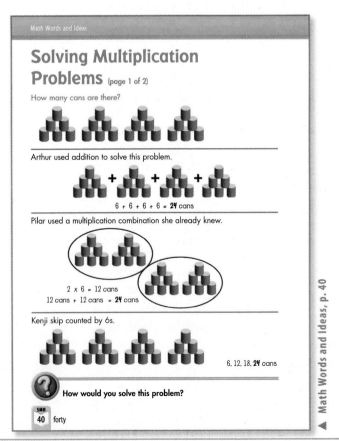

▲ Math Words and Ideas, p. 40

▲ Math Words and Ideas, p. 41

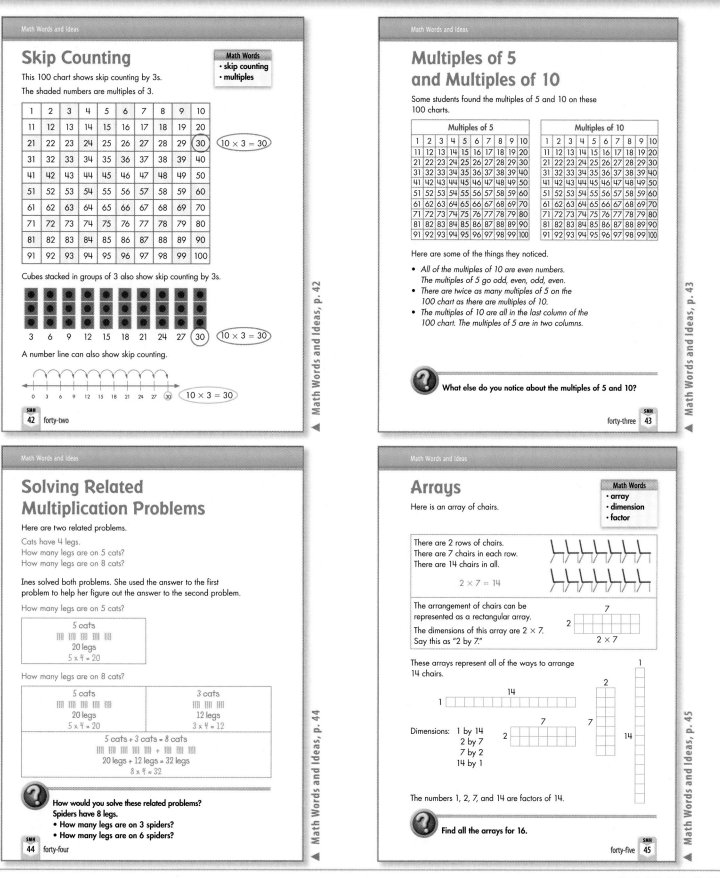

Skip Counting

This 100 chart shows skip counting by 3s.
The shaded numbers are multiples of 3.

Math Words
- skip counting
- multiples

1	2	3	4	5	6	7	8	9	10
11	12	13	14	15	16	17	18	19	20
21	22	23	24	25	26	27	28	29	30
31	32	33	34	35	36	37	38	39	40
41	42	43	44	45	46	47	48	49	50
51	52	53	54	55	56	57	58	59	60
61	62	63	64	65	66	67	68	69	70
71	72	73	74	75	76	77	78	79	80
81	82	83	84	85	86	87	88	89	90
91	92	93	94	95	96	97	98	99	100

$10 \times 3 = 30$

Cubes stacked in groups of 3 also show skip counting by 3s.

3 6 9 12 15 18 21 24 27 30 $10 \times 3 = 30$

A number line can also show skip counting.

0 3 6 9 12 15 18 21 24 27 30 $10 \times 3 = 30$

SMH 42 forty-two

◄ Math Words and Ideas, p. 42

Multiples of 5 and Multiples of 10

Some students found the multiples of 5 and 10 on these 100 charts.

Multiples of 5

1	2	3	4	5	6	7	8	9	10
11	12	13	14	15	16	17	18	19	20
21	22	23	24	25	26	27	28	29	30
31	32	33	34	35	36	37	38	39	40
41	42	43	44	45	46	47	48	49	50
51	52	53	54	55	56	57	58	59	60
61	62	63	64	65	66	67	68	69	70
71	72	73	74	75	76	77	78	79	80
81	82	83	84	85	86	87	88	89	90
91	92	93	94	95	96	97	98	99	100

Multiples of 10

1	2	3	4	5	6	7	8	9	10
11	12	13	14	15	16	17	18	19	20
21	22	23	24	25	26	27	28	29	30
31	32	33	34	35	36	37	38	39	40
41	42	43	44	45	46	47	48	49	50
51	52	53	54	55	56	57	58	59	60
61	62	63	64	65	66	67	68	69	70
71	72	73	74	75	76	77	78	79	80
81	82	83	84	85	86	87	88	89	90
91	92	93	94	95	96	97	98	99	100

Here are some of the things they noticed.

- All of the multiples of 10 are even numbers. The multiples of 5 go odd, even, odd, even.
- There are twice as many multiples of 5 on the 100 chart as there are multiples of 10.
- The multiples of 10 are all in the last column of the 100 chart. The multiples of 5 are in two columns.

? What else do you notice about the multiples of 5 and 10?

forty-three **SMH 43**

◄ Math Words and Ideas, p. 43

Solving Related Multiplication Problems

Here are two related problems.

Cats have 4 legs.
How many legs are on 5 cats?
How many legs are on 8 cats?

Ines solved both problems. She used the answer to the first problem to help her figure out the answer to the second problem.

How many legs are on 5 cats?

5 cats
20 legs
$5 \times 4 = 20$

How many legs are on 8 cats?

5 cats	3 cats
20 legs	12 legs
$5 \times 4 = 20$	$3 \times 4 = 12$

5 cats + 3 cats = 8 cats
20 legs + 12 legs = 32 legs
$8 \times 4 = 32$

? How would you solve these related problems?
Spiders have 8 legs.
- How many legs are on 3 spiders?
- How many legs are on 6 spiders?

SMH 44 forty-four

◄ Math Words and Ideas, p. 44

Arrays

Here is an array of chairs.

Math Words
- array
- dimension
- factor

There are 2 rows of chairs.
There are 7 chairs in each row.
There are 14 chairs in all.

$2 \times 7 = 14$

The arrangement of chairs can be represented as a rectangular array.

The dimensions of this array are 2×7.
Say this as "2 by 7."

2×7

These arrays represent all of the ways to arrange 14 chairs.

Dimensions: 1 by 14
2 by 7
7 by 2
14 by 1

The numbers 1, 2, 7, and 14 are factors of 14.

? Find all the arrays for 16.

forty-five **SMH 45**

◄ Math Words and Ideas, p. 45

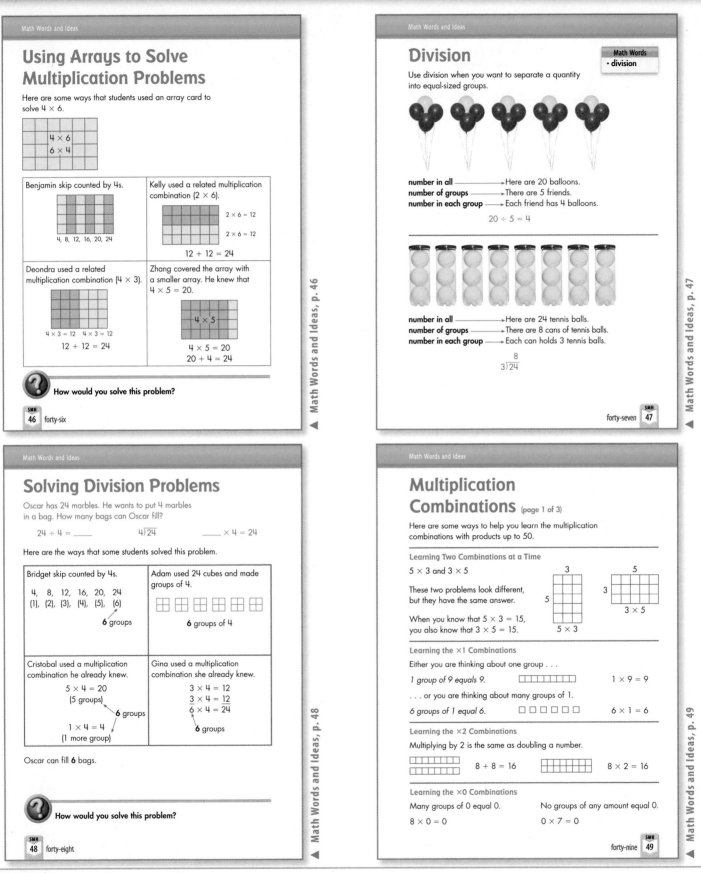

Using Arrays to Solve Multiplication Problems

Here are some ways that students used an array card to solve 4×6.

$$4 \times 6$$
$$6 \times 4$$

Benjamin skip counted by 4s.	Kelly used a related multiplication combination (2×6).
4, 8, 12, 16, 20, 24	$2 \times 6 = 12$ $2 \times 6 = 12$ $12 + 12 = 24$
Deondra used a related multiplication combination (4×3).	Zhang covered the array with a smaller array. He knew that $4 \times 5 = 20$.
$4 \times 3 = 12$ $4 \times 3 = 12$ $12 + 12 = 24$	4×5 $4 \times 5 = 20$ $20 + 4 = 24$

? How would you solve this problem?

SMH 46 forty-six

Math Words and Ideas, p. 46

Division

Math Words
• division

Use division when you want to separate a quantity into equal-sized groups.

number in all ⟶ Here are 20 balloons.
number of groups ⟶ There are 5 friends.
number in each group ⟶ Each friend has 4 balloons.

$$20 \div 5 = 4$$

number in all ⟶ Here are 24 tennis balls.
number of groups ⟶ There are 8 cans of tennis balls.
number in each group ⟶ Each can holds 3 tennis balls.

$$3 \overline{)24}^{\,8}$$

forty-seven **SMH 47**

Math Words and Ideas, p. 47

Solving Division Problems

Oscar has 24 marbles. He wants to put 4 marbles in a bag. How many bags can Oscar fill?

$$24 \div 4 = \underline{\quad} \qquad 4\overline{)24} \qquad \underline{\quad} \times 4 = 24$$

Here are the ways that some students solved this problem.

Bridget skip counted by 4s.	Adam used 24 cubes and made groups of 4.
4, 8, 12, 16, 20, 24 (1), (2), (3), (4), (5), (6) **6** groups	**6** groups of 4
Cristobal used a multiplication combination he already knew.	Gina used a multiplication combination she already knew.
$5 \times 4 = 20$ (5 groups) **6** groups $1 \times 4 = 4$ (1 more group)	$3 \times 4 = 12$ $3 \times 4 = 12$ $6 \times 4 = 24$ **6** groups

Oscar can fill **6** bags.

? How would you solve this problem?

SMH 48 forty-eight

Math Words and Ideas, p. 48

Multiplication Combinations (page 1 of 3)

Here are some ways to help you learn the multiplication combinations with products up to 50.

Learning Two Combinations at a Time

5×3 and 3×5

These two problems look different, but they have the same answer.

When you know that $5 \times 3 = 15$, you also know that $3 \times 5 = 15$.

$$5 \times 3 \qquad 3 \times 5$$

Learning the ×1 Combinations

Either you are thinking about one group . . .

1 group of 9 equals 9. $1 \times 9 = 9$

. . . or you are thinking about many groups of 1.

6 groups of 1 equal 6. $6 \times 1 = 6$

Learning the ×2 Combinations

Multiplying by 2 is the same as doubling a number.

$8 + 8 = 16$ $8 \times 2 = 16$

Learning the ×0 Combinations

Many groups of 0 equal 0.   No groups of any amount equal 0.

$8 \times 0 = 0$ $0 \times 7 = 0$

forty-nine **SMH 49**

Math Words and Ideas, p. 49

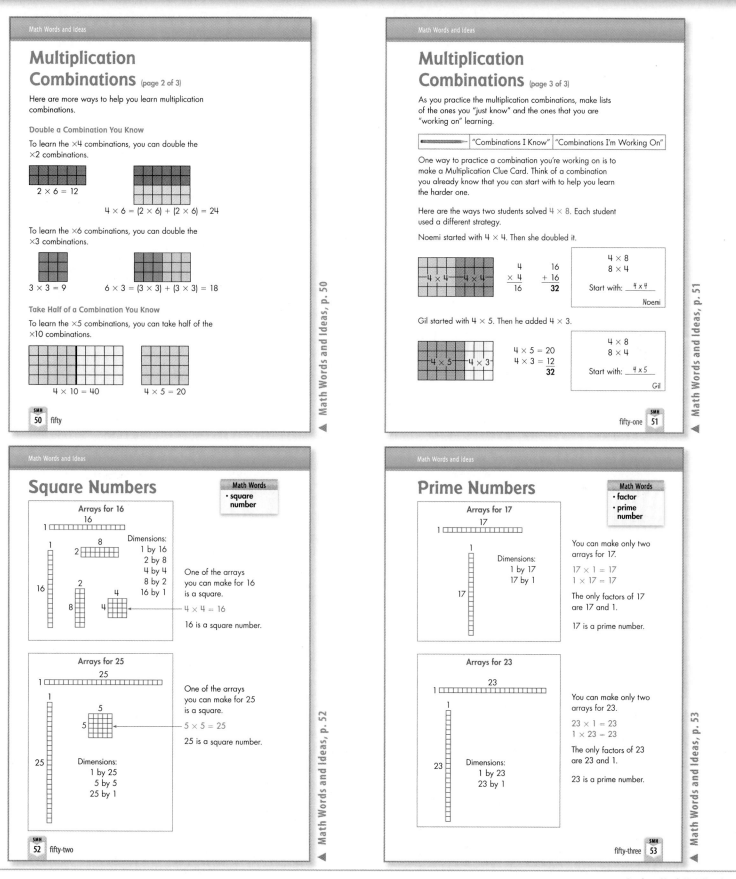

Multiplication Combinations (page 2 of 3)

Here are more ways to help you learn multiplication combinations.

Double a Combination You Know

To learn the ×4 combinations, you can double the ×2 combinations.

2 × 6 = 12

4 × 6 = (2 × 6) + (2 × 6) = 24

To learn the ×6 combinations, you can double the ×3 combinations.

3 × 3 = 9

6 × 3 = (3 × 3) + (3 × 3) = 18

Take Half of a Combination You Know

To learn the ×5 combinations, you can take half of the ×10 combinations.

4 × 10 = 40

4 × 5 = 20

SMH 50 fifty

◀ Math Words and Ideas, p. 50

Multiplication Combinations (page 3 of 3)

As you practice the multiplication combinations, make lists of the ones you "just know" and the ones that you are "working on" learning.

| "Combinations I Know" | "Combinations I'm Working On" |

One way to practice a combination you're working on is to make a Multiplication Clue Card. Think of a combination you already know that you can start with to help you learn the harder one.

Here are the ways two students solved 4 × 8. Each student used a different strategy.

Noemi started with 4 × 4. Then she doubled it.

4 × 4   4 × 4

$\begin{array}{r} 4 \\ \times\ 4 \\ \hline 16 \end{array}$ $\begin{array}{r} 16 \\ +\ 16 \\ \hline \mathbf{32} \end{array}$

4 × 8
8 × 4
Start with: _4 x 4_
Noemi

Gil started with 4 × 5. Then he added 4 × 3.

4 × 5   4 × 3

4 × 5 = 20
4 × 3 = $\underline{12}$
32

4 × 8
8 × 4
Start with: _4 x 5_
Gil

fifty-one **SMH 51**

◀ Math Words and Ideas, p. 51

Square Numbers

Math Words
• square number

Arrays for 16

16
1

8
2

1
16

2
8

4
4

Dimensions:
1 by 16
2 by 8
4 by 4
8 by 2
16 by 1

One of the arrays you can make for 16 is a square.

4 × 4 = 16

16 is a square number.

Arrays for 25

25
1

1
25

5
5

One of the arrays you can make for 25 is a square.

5 × 5 = 25

25 is a square number.

Dimensions:
1 by 25
5 by 5
25 by 1

SMH 52 fifty-two

◀ Math Words and Ideas, p. 52

Prime Numbers

Math Words
• factor
• prime number

Arrays for 17

17
1

1
17

Dimensions:
1 by 17
17 by 1

You can make only two arrays for 17.

17 × 1 = 17
1 × 17 = 17

The only factors of 17 are 17 and 1.

17 is a prime number.

Arrays for 23

23
1

1
23

Dimensions:
1 by 23
23 by 1

You can make only two arrays for 23.

23 × 1 = 23
1 × 23 = 23

The only factors of 23 are 23 and 1.

23 is a prime number.

fifty-three **SMH 53**

◀ Math Words and Ideas, p. 53

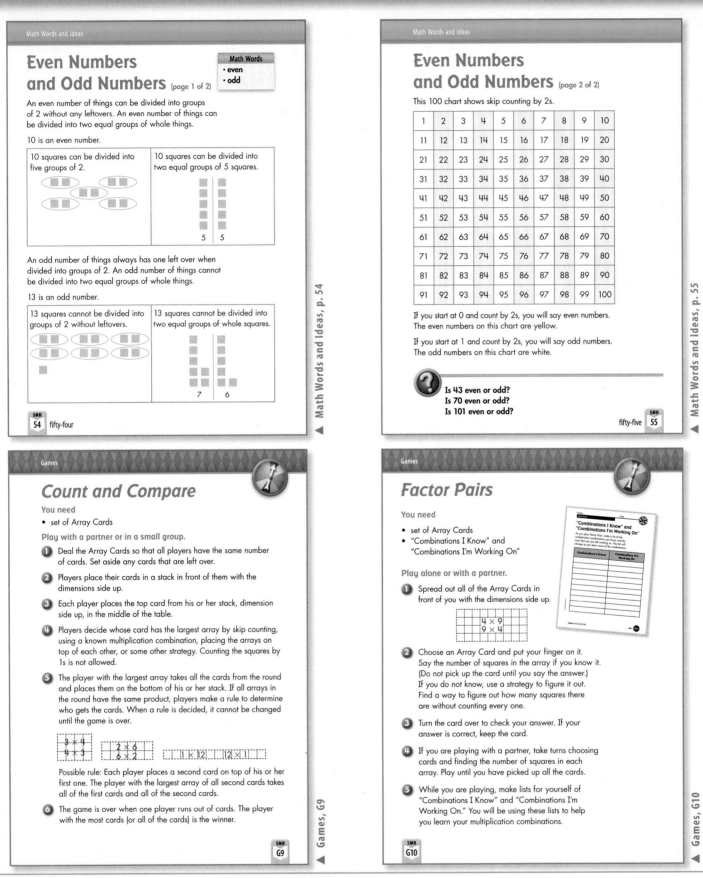

Math Words and Ideas

Even Numbers and Odd Numbers (page 1 of 2)

Math Words
- even
- odd

An even number of things can be divided into groups of 2 without any leftovers. An even number of things can be divided into two equal groups of whole things.

10 is an even number.

10 squares can be divided into five groups of 2.	10 squares can be divided into two equal groups of 5 squares.
	5 5

An odd number of things always has one left over when divided into groups of 2. An odd number of things cannot be divided into two equal groups of whole things.

13 is an odd number.

13 squares cannot be divided into groups of 2 without leftovers.	13 squares cannot be divided into two equal groups of whole squares.
	7 6

SMH 54 fifty-four

◀ Math Words and Ideas, p. 54

Math Words and Ideas

Even Numbers and Odd Numbers (page 2 of 2)

This 100 chart shows skip counting by 2s.

1	2	3	4	5	6	7	8	9	10
11	12	13	14	15	16	17	18	19	20
21	22	23	24	25	26	27	28	29	30
31	32	33	34	35	36	37	38	39	40
41	42	43	44	45	46	47	48	49	50
51	52	53	54	55	56	57	58	59	60
61	62	63	64	65	66	67	68	69	70
71	72	73	74	75	76	77	78	79	80
81	82	83	84	85	86	87	88	89	90
91	92	93	94	95	96	97	98	99	100

If you start at 0 and count by 2s, you will say even numbers. The even numbers on this chart are yellow.

If you start at 1 and count by 2s, you will say odd numbers. The odd numbers on this chart are white.

? Is 43 even or odd?
Is 70 even or odd?
Is 101 even or odd?

fifty-five **SMH 55**

◀ Math Words and Ideas, p. 55

Games

Count and Compare

You need
- set of Array Cards

Play with a partner or in a small group.

1. Deal the Array Cards so that all players have the same number of cards. Set aside any cards that are left over.

2. Players place their cards in a stack in front of them with the dimensions side up.

3. Each player places the top card from his or her stack, dimension side up, in the middle of the table.

4. Players decide whose card has the largest array by skip counting, using a known multiplication combination, placing the arrays on top of each other, or some other strategy. Counting the squares by 1s is not allowed.

5. The player with the largest array takes all the cards from the round and places them on the bottom of his or her stack. If all arrays in the round have the same product, players make a rule to determine who gets the cards. When a rule is decided, it cannot be changed until the game is over.

Possible rule: Each player places a second card on top of his or her first one. The player with the largest array of all second cards takes all of the first cards and all of the second cards.

6. The game is over when one player runs out of cards. The player with the most cards (or all of the cards) is the winner.

SMH G9

◀ Games, G9

Games

Factor Pairs

You need
- set of Array Cards
- "Combinations I Know" and "Combinations I'm Working On"

Play alone or with a partner.

1. Spread out all of the Array Cards in front of you with the dimensions side up.

2. Choose an Array Card and put your finger on it. Say the number of squares in the array if you know it. (Do not pick up the card until you say the answer.) If you do not know, use a strategy to figure it out. Find a way to figure out how many squares there are without counting every one.

3. Turn the card over to check your answer. If your answer is correct, keep the card.

4. If you are playing with a partner, take turns choosing cards and finding the number of squares in each array. Play until you have picked up all the cards.

5. While you are playing, make lists for yourself of "Combinations I Know" and "Combinations I'm Working On." You will be using these lists to help you learn your multiplication combinations.

SMH G10

◀ Games, G10

Missing Factors (page 1 of 2)

You need

- set of Array Cards
- *Missing Factors* Recording Sheet

Play alone or with a partner. This game is a variation of Factor Pairs.

1 Spread out all of the Array Cards in front of you with the product side up.

2 Choose an Array Card. One dimension is written for you. The *missing factor* is the other dimension. You must say what the missing factor is. For example, if you choose an Array Card that has the product of 16, and one dimension is 2, the missing factor is 8.

| 16 | 2 |

3 Turn the card over to check your answer. If your answer is correct, keep the card. If your answer is not correct, return the card to the set of Array Cards, dimensions side up.

| | | 2 x 8 | | | |
| | | 8 x 2 | | | |

Missing Factors (page 2 of 2)

4 On the *Missing Factors* Recording Sheet, write an equation to go with each array you keep. Circle the missing factor. For example:

$2 \times \textcircled{8} = 16$ or $16 \div 2 = \textcircled{8}$

5 If you are playing with a partner, take turns choosing cards until all the cards with products still showing have been picked up.

6 When there are only cards with dimensions sides showing, take turns pointing to a card and saying what is on the other side (the product), keeping the cards when your answers are correct. The player with the most cards wins.

Practicing with Multiplication Cards
(page 1 of 2)

You need

- 6 sheets of Multiplication Cards
- Array Cards
- scissors
- paper clip
- resealable plastic bag

Play with a partner.

1 Cut out each Multiplication Card and write your initials and the product on the back. Check each product with a calculator, your Array Cards, or someone else's help.

2 Ask someone to show you the front of each Multiplication Card. Say the product as quickly as you can. If you get it right away, put the card in a pile of combinations that you "just know." If you have to stop and figure it out, put it into a different pile of combinations that you are "working on."

3 Paper clip your "just know" cards together and put them in the plastic bag.

Practicing with Multiplication Cards
(page 2 of 2)

4 Look at each card in your "working on" pile. Think of an easy multiplication combination that you already know that can help you remember this one. Write it on the line that says "Start with _____."

| 5×6 |
| 6×5 |
| Start with 5×5 |

5 Practice each of the cards in your "working on" pile at least three times.

6 Put all your cards back together (including the ones you "just know") and go through them again. Keep practicing over the next few weeks until you have no more cards in your "working on" pile.

Index